STORIES of the
BOOK of BOOKS

Grace W. McGavran

Stories of the
BOOK OF BOOKS

By
GRACE W. McGAVRAN

Cover Design and Endpapers by
THEODORE GUERIN

FRIENDSHIP PRESS · NEW YORK

GRACE W. McGAVRAN, who wrote *Stories of the Book of Books,* was born at Damoh, India, the daughter and granddaughter of missionary families. She came to America for her education, taking her B.A. at Butler College, Indianapolis, and her M.A. at Boston University.

From the beginning Miss McGavran was interested in religious and missionary work. For several years she was director of religious education in the First Congregational Church at Topeka, Kansas. Later she served with the Missionary Education Department of the United Christian Missionary Society.

Miss McGavran then turned to free-lance writing, giving special attention to missionary and world friendship stories, articles, and units of study for children. She is the author of four books previously published by the Friendship Press, *Far Round the World* and *We Gather Together* for the junior age group, and *Fig Tree Village* and *Mpengo of the Congo* for primary children.

COPYRIGHT, 1947, BY FRIENDSHIP PRESS, INC.

Printed in the United States of America

TO MY THREE BIG NEPHEWS
MALCOLM
TED
TAD

CONTENTS

Part I: HOW OUR BIBLE CAME TO BE   1

Part II: THE BIBLE INTO ALL THE WORLD   7

1:   *The Gospels of Lindesfarne*   7
     England (690-750)

2:   *The Cost of an English Bible*   13
     England (1522-1536)

3:   *Reading the Great Bible*   20
     England (after 1536)

4:   *The Church That Had No Bible*   24
     India (1806)

5:   *Biscuits into Bibles*   28
     New Hebrides (1848-1872)

6:   *In an Unknown Tongue*   34
     Canada (1855-1864)

7:   *When the* Morning Star *Sailed*   40
     Gilbert Islands (1856-1894)

8:   *The Bible Rides the Western Plains*   46
     United States (1860)

9:   *White Sails and Blue Sea*   51
     New Zealand (1874)

10: *The Little Slave Girl of Madagascar*   55
     Madagascar (1882)

11: *The Word of God Is My Sword*   63
     New Zealand

12: *The Bible in Their Hearts*   70
     Poland

13: *The Black Magic of Don Cornelio*   78
     Central America

14: *The Strength to Be Good*   86
     Korea

15: *The Search among Thieves*   93
     Paraguay

16: *Four Chickens and Twice Fifty Miles*   99
     Africa

17: *A Miner Strikes Pay Dirt*   103
        United States

18: *The Man Who Surprised His Family*   108
        Japan

19: *Teresa's Great Big Holy Book*   114
        Mexico

20: *Follow the Line*   121
        United States

21: *Singers in the Dark*   125
        Peru

22: *Two Gunmen and a Bible*   134
        United States

Part III: INCIDENTS ABOUT THE BIBLE   138

1: *Singing the Bible*   138
        Africa

2: *The Bible a Gateway*   142
        China

3: *Seven Pieces of Silk*   144
        India

4: *The Prize Bible*   149
        India

5: *The Bible Bought by Music*   153
        United States

6: *The Dusted Bible*   156
        United States

7: *The Blind Leper*   159
        Latin America

8: *Headaches of a Translator*   162

9: *Translation on Top of a Ladder*   165
        Northern Rhodesia

Part IV: BIBLE WORDS IN MANY TONGUES   167

1: *The Lord's Prayer*   167
        IN THE ENGLAND OF A THOUSAND YEARS
        AGO, 167
        FROM TYNDALE'S VERSION, 168
        A MODERN TRANSLATION, 168

WITH RESPONSE, 169
IN FRENCH, 170
IN SPANISH, 170

2: *The Twenty-third Psalm*   170
PARAPHRASE FOR NAVAJO INDIANS, 170
PARAPHRASE BY A JUNIOR HIGH GROUP, 171

3: *James 1: 22 in Nine Languages*   171

4: *Some Verses to Read*   172

5: *Talking Birch Bark*   173
CREE ALPHABET AND A VERSE IN CREE, 173

Part V: WORSHIP MATERIALS   176

1: *Poems and Hymns*   176
THE WORD OF GOD, 176
SHIPS, 177
BOOK OF BOOKS, 178
THE BIBLE HELPS ME, 178
LORD, THY WORD ABIDETH, 179
THE BIBLE IS A TREASURE BOOK, 179
FOR STORIES FINE AND TRUE, 180
FOR THY GREAT BOOK OF STORIES, 180

2: *Prayers*   181
UPON RECEIVING A GIFT OF A BIBLE, 181
AFTER EXAMINING A BIBLE IN ANOTHER
    LANGUAGE, 181
AFTER GATHERING AN OFFERING TO SEND
    BIBLES TO OTHERS, 181
BEFORE USING THE BIBLE IN CLASS, 182
AFTER READING FROM THE BIBLE, 182
BECAUSE WE HAVE THE BIBLE, 182
FOR TRANSLATORS, 182

PART I: HOW OUR BIBLE CAME TO BE

Back, back, before the days of Abraham and Isaac, there were no books. But there were stories and storytellers. In the evenings the shepherd people sat outside their tents and listened to the stories. For years and years and years, stories were passed along from father to son. The people did not miss books, because they could not yet read or write. They liked to hear how God had made the world and everything in it. They learned how their people had come to know God.

Some years before the time of Abraham and Isaac, the knowledge of reading and writing came to the people of their country. The first writing was done on clay tablets. Their first books were scrolls, made of long strips of sheepskin. The writing was done in columns, from right to left, along the length of the strip of skin. Only a few priests and scribes could read and write. They wrote on the scrolls the stories that had been told for long years around the campfires—how God had made the world, how he had led his people and given them laws by which to live. The stories were carefully copied from scroll to scroll. The Old Testament stories came from the scrolls of long ago.

During Old Testament times, before Jesus came to the world, preachers spoke to the people of Israel, or the Jewish people, as they were later called. These preachers were known as prophets and they gave their people messages from God. The stories and messages of the prophets were written. You will find many of them in the Old Testament. You will also find the book of hymns that the people used in worshiping God. It is called the *Psalms*.

Then Jesus came to earth and preached and taught. After his life on earth had ended, his disciples and friends told over and over the things that he did and said. At first a few hundred, then thousands and tens of thousands of people became followers of Jesus. They wanted to know his story and his teachings. So books were written to give the story of Jesus' life and to tell of his teaching. These books are called the Gospels, which means "good messages." You will find them in the first part of the New Testament.

Paul was one of the greatest of the early followers of Jesus. He traveled far and wide to spread the teachings of Jesus. He founded Christian churches in the towns and cities where he visited. As he traveled, Paul wrote letters to the new Christians to encourage and comfort them. His letters were read again and again. They were copied and sent around to be read in other Christian churches. The people who heard them felt as if Paul were talking to them. You can read some of Paul's letters today in that part of the New Testament called the *Epistles*.

As the centuries rolled by, wars and plagues swept over Europe and Asia. Towns and cities were destroyed, and with them their books and scrolls. Some Bibles were lost forever. Lately scholars have taken to exploring the sites of long-forgotten towns. In the ruins of old buildings they have  come upon old copies of the Bible. In the drifting sands of Egypt they have found scraps of parchment that carried on them chapters of the Bible. Some of these scraps have been used in making new versions of the Bible.

In the midst of the wars the most peaceful places in all of Europe were the monasteries where the monks lived. Working away inside their quiet rooms, shut off from the world in their safe buildings, the monks made the most beautiful handwritten books the world has ever known. They wrote on  sheets of parchment, which was made of carefully prepared sheepskin. The books they made were copies of the Bible. The Bible was their treasure. They decorated the pages with capital letters and with tiny drawings, in gold and blues and reds and greens.

The monks traveled far and wide to carry the story of Jesus. When they went to a new country, they took a handmade Bible with them. Some monks, sent by Pope Gregory, went from Rome to England, then a little known island. They carried  with them a Bible in Latin. So did the monks who went to Germany and to other countries of which little was known. The monks and their Bibles had a great influence on the people to whom they went. Slowly, slowly, over the years, those people learned what the monks taught and they became Christians. They could not learn quickly or well, because the Bibles were so few and because they were written in Latin. Only the monks could have those precious handmade volumes of the Bible.

At last the printing press was invented. The first book to be printed on it was the Bible. Now many copies of the Bible could be made and many people could own the book. The Latin Bible was the one most widely used at that time. But soon translations of it were made into the languages spoken by the people of the different countries of Europe. Tyndale translated the New Testament into English, had it printed in Germany, and smuggled into England. The leaders of the church were furious. They destroyed as many copies of Tyndale's New Testament as they could find. Some years later they had Tyndale arrested and put to death. But they could not stop the use of the Bible in English.

Other translators of the Bible into English followed Tyndale. In the forty years following his death several new translations were made. The church leaders began to show less opposition to the people using the Bible. But the number of copies printed was still small. There were not nearly enough to go around. The king ordered that copies of the version called "The Great Bible" should be placed in every church in England. Lest the eager people take away the Bibles to read at home, the books were chained to the pulpits.

In 1600 there was argument about which
English Bible was best. King James I
ordered scholars to prepare a new version.
This was done, and then many people
could own the Bible, hold it in their hands
and read it. But some wanted more than
this. They wanted to be free to worship as
they wished. So the Pilgrim Fathers left England and sailed
for the New World. With them went the Bible, into the
wilderness of New England. It was their guide during the
hard days of building new homes for themselves.

Settlers streamed into the new country of
America. Villages grew into towns and
towns into cities. Year after year fresh
parts of the country were opened up.
Groups of settlers raised homes far from
towns or churches. To them came the hardy
circuit riders—preachers who rode their
sturdy horses in a great circuit, stopping at settlement after
settlement to carry the Bible message to the people. As the
pioneers pushed ever westward, along with them went the
hardy border preacher, the circuit rider with the Bible in his
saddlebags.

Now America is settled from coast to
coast. In every part of the land there are
homes and churches, out in the country as
well as in towns and cities. Can you imag-
ine a church today without a Bible? Or a
church service in which there is no reading
or quoting from the Word of God? Or a
Christian group that does not study the Bible or listen to its
words? From North to South, from Hudson Bay to Mexico,

from East to West, from the Atlantic to the Pacific, the Bible is found in the churches of America.

Not only in the churches is the Bible found. It is in Christian homes all over the land. It can be seen in the hands of grown-ups and of children. Perhaps the Book is a big one—a family Bible. Perhaps it is a brand-new Bible that a little girl has been given as she goes from the primary into the junior department, or it may be a Bible with big print for Grandfather, who is not seeing as well as he once did. Anyone who wishes to buy one can have a Bible. The Bible is in our homes today.

PART II: THE BIBLE INTO ALL THE WORLD

I: The Gospels of Lindesfarne

England (690-750)

IN THE blue-gray waters off the coast of England there lay an island, fair as a dream. The breakers crashed upon it in storm, and the wind whipped it, and the rain drenched it. But on days when the sun shone it lay like a jewel in the sea and the little waves crept up softly to touch it with their quickly drawn-back fingers.

The name of the island was like music upon the lips, and when people spoke of Lindesfarne, contentment came upon them. Later it was called the Holy Isle. Yet which name is better, each must judge for himself.

On that island the body of St. Cuthbert lay, kept, as was the custom, in a place of honor in a chapel. For the monks who lived there loved the memory of this missionary monk and rejoiced that the body of their saint was with them.

Back in the years between and around A.D. 690 and A.D. 700 (and that is more than a thousand years ago), there lived on Lindesfarne a monk named Eadfrith. He was bishop of the monks who dwelt there. The eyes of Eadfrith were calm and full of courage. They needed to be so, for the times were full of danger and none knew when fire and death and terror would descend upon the peaceful community. The Viking raiders from Europe's mainland came stealthily, in their swift dragonboats, and no one would be aware of them until their fierce battle cry rang out.

But if the eyes of Eadfrith were full of courage, they were

full of dreams as well—dreams of a day when men would lay down their swords and spears and follow a Leader whose banner is love.

As Eadfrith ruled his tiny community, he worked, taking fair sheets of precious vellum and copying on them, with infinite patience, the words of the Gospels, whose story tells of the life on earth of our Lord Christ Jesus. For how shall swords be laid down unless the knowledge of Jesus, who can save the world from its sorrow, be spread abroad?

Day after day, week after week, Eadfrith worked, making each letter with all the skill he possessed. Some letters were plain; others, and especially the letters at the beginnings of the pages, were glorious with color, holding within their curves delicately wrought pictures of saints and angels.

Day after day, week after week, he worked, making the letters of each word with clear and beautiful shape. And so the words followed one after another—words in the Latin tongue, copied faithfully from the parchment volumes that were the monks' only copies of the Bible.

The seasons rolled by. Spring scattered blossoms on the storm-swept grass. They were matched with the color that blossomed under Eadfrith's brushes in fanciful flower designs around the great capital letters of the Gospel of *Matthew*. Summer and autumn fled past and winter came. Still the patient fingers moved slowly and accurately across the pages. Eadfrith had need to warm them now and again, lest they be stiff with the bitter cold and mar the beauty of the work.

At last the copying of the Gospels was ended. The sheets were laid together by a hand other than Eadfrith's, for his life was finished. The year 724 had come and Ethelwald was bishop. He ordered the book of the Gospels made stiff on the outside, so that the inner sheets might be protected. Billfrith, the anchorite, took the book. With all his smith's cunning he adorned the cover with gold and with silver and with precious stones.

When Billfrith had finished his work and had touched the book lovingly and reverently for the last time, the Gospels in all their beauty were carried to the Shrine of Lindesfarne. There beside the body of St. Cuthbert they were laid.

Then the lips of the monks moved in silent thanksgiving that nothing had hindered the completion of the book that Eadfrith in joy and devotion had prepared.

Who knows, now that a thousand and more years have passed, how often the precious pages were turned by reverent hands, and the long, flowing Latin words were sounded by reading lips while the listening monks gave thanks for the Word of God? The Gospels were the monks' treasure and delight through calm and storm for more than a hundred years.

Then came that which they had feared. The dragonboats of the raiding Vikings were seen once more, and in fear and trembling the monks knew that fire and ruin and death would come stealing across the waters, even to Lindesfarne.

The fair and beautiful book was hastily lifted by the monks from its place and was carefully wrapped. The body of St. Cuthbert was bound up for a long journey. Across the gray waters in their little boat went the monks, secretly, that none might know of the double treasure that they carried through the moonlight to England.

Up and down the land the monks wandered, seeking safe haven for their treasure. Back to Lindesfarne they dared not go, for there was no safety in that place, nor would there be for years to come.

Even in England danger threatened. The raiding Vikings were there also. The monks determined to seek another isle where they might live and work in peace.

So they boarded a ship, bound for Ireland—that fair, green

isle. Only a tiny ship it was! And the sea so great! With
them the monks carried the Gospels of Eadfrith's copying
and the body of St. Cuthbert, their patron saint.

As the ship beat its way onward, a frightful storm arose.
The wind and the waves tore at it, carrying off all that was
movable. The monks wept as they struggled for their
lives. Before their eyes they saw the precious Gospels swept
away, swallowed up in the towering waves that threatened
to destroy them also. The body of St. Cuthbert and themselves they managed to save.

They were driven back to the shores of England, glad to
escape with their lives. One and another said piously that it
might be that St. Cuthbert willed not to have his body rest
on Irish soil.

However that may be, the monks gathered on the sea-
shore, while the waves were still beating high. They gazed
with longing into the wild waters that held their treasure—
their precious Gospels.

Now among the great masses of kelp and the welter of
wreckage that the waves thrust forward and pulled back
from shore there washed a bundle that had been upon that
little ship. The storm-lashed waves carried the bundle and
the bits of plank and the seaweed and the odds and ends
higher and higher and finally tossed them up beyond their
own withdrawing. There they lay, caught among the rocks.

There came a morning when the storm died down to a
whisper, worn out with its own violence. In the same day
there was a low, low tide. Then down to the shore came the
people of the near-by villages, and with them the monks, to
search among the rocks for whatever of value might have
been tossed up by the tempest.

They found masts and bits of sail and sturdy timbers
from vessels that the storm had beaten to pieces. The villagers rejoiced at the treasure. But the monks cared nothing

for such things. With no real hope, they searched the dripping shore, till of a sudden they came upon a bundle wedged tightly between two rocks.

What a shout then was raised! Could it be that here was that which they had lost? Or was it a bundle of garments or other books? The monks gathered around it.

Curiously the villagers watched them open the bundle. Not one of them had to that day seen anything like that which lay within the water-soaked wrappings—great pages of vellum, bound in a cover studded with gold and silver and jewels that sparkled under the sun like the great sea itself. And on the pages lines of black writing with wondrous bright pictures in blue and green and red and gold.

"All praise to God!" whispered the monks. "For that our Gospels be safe!"

"And not even damaged!" murmured one. "See, only a few of the sheets have been wet by the water of the sea!"

So once more the great book of the Gospels and the body of St. Cuthbert resumed their journeyings. The monks carried them from one place to another as they themselves wandered homeless through the land. But they made no further attempt to take them to Ireland, although some of their number did indeed go there, and took with them the art of making the beautiful books.

At last, upon a day, they came to the monastery in the town of Chester-le-street and found refuge there for themselves and their treasures. The monks of that place looked with awe upon the work of Eadfrith, the bishop, and of Billfrith, the anchorite. They examined the writing with love and delight, for they could see that a master hand and infinite love and patience had wrought the work.

The monks of Chester-le-street were not learned. They spoke the rough Anglo-Saxon tongue, which was the English of that day. But few of them could read the Latin words, though the hunger to read lay deep and strong in their hearts.

Then spoke up Aldred who was one of themselves. He offered a plan and asked the consent of the monks of Lindesfarne to it. After much thought and prayer, consent was given.

The apple trees flowered and the murmur of bees filled the blossom-scented meadows. Yet Aldred heard none of it. Nor yet did he hear the sweet trilling of the birds, mad with the joy of springtime.

He sat with the fair pages of the book of the Gospels before him. And in the spaces between the lines of Latin words—spaces so broad that they seemed almost to have been made so for this purpose—he wrote the English meaning of the Latin words.

Line after line, page after page, Gospel after Gospel, he set them all in, in his own Anglo-Saxon tongue.

For how can swords be laid down, and spears be set to rest unless the knowledge of One who can save the world from its sin and from its sorrow be spread abroad? And how shall the story be spread unless each one can read it in his own tongue?

Storms beat upon Lindesfarne. Bees hum among the apple trees of ancient Chester-le-street. And in a special place in London where the people of England keep their dearest treasures, you may even today see the ancient volume. Your eyes may rest upon the very words that Eadfrith and Aldred wrote, more than a thousand years ago, in the Gospels of Lindesfarne, the Holy Isle.

2: The Cost of an English Bible

England (1522-1536)

YOUNG William Tyndale felt he was in great good luck. His work at the university was finished and he had a comfortable position. He was to be tutor to the two sons of Sir John Walsh.

Besides teaching the two little boys to read and write, he was chaplain to the household. He had to read the daily prayers and to conduct services.

In those days people loved to argue about religious matters. Martin Luther, over in Germany, had defied the pope and started the Reformation, and that was always a fine subject for argument. England was still a Catholic country, but Tyndale, like Luther, thought more highly of the Bible and what it said than of the pope and what he said. So the arguments around Sir John Walsh's table were lively, although more people sided against the young tutor than with him.

Tyndale liked to preach in the village churches. And the people loved to hear him. He would read the Bible to them, putting its Latin words into English. He would explain the Bible teaching. When word went around that young William Tyndale was to preach, the people gathered in crowds to listen. But alas, the older clergymen did not care at all for William's preaching. He was in trouble with them all the time. He decided that if he had to choose between preaching what these older clergymen believed and what the Bible taught, he would choose to follow the Bible.

"Ah," thought Tyndale, "if only we had a copy of the New Testament printed in English, so that people could have it and read it and know what it says. That's what we need."

He had an idea. "I'll go to London," thought Tyndale, "and I'll ask the Bishop of London if I may make a translation of the New Testament. If he says it is all right, the printers will be willing to print it." Tyndale didn't say it out loud, but he knew that if the bishop did not say that it was all right, no printer in England would dare touch the job!

Up to London went Tyndale, full of hope.

He was an excellent scholar and knew Greek and Hebrew. He loved the Bible and wanted the people to have it in English. The translating wouldn't cost the bishop a penny. All Tyndale needed was a quiet room in the bishop's household for working, and permission to make the translation.

But the bishop didn't say it was all right. He thought it was wrong to put the Bible into English for the common people. He had no intention of helping with any such project.

"My home is full," said the bishop to the disappointed young man. "I really cannot make you a member of my household. I have more mouths to feed now than I can manage."

All of which, of course, was the bishop's way of saying that he would not give permission for the translation.

"Oh, well," said Tyndale to himself, as he walked slowly away from the bishop's residence, "I can do some preaching and make the translation at the same time."

And this he started to do. He preached on Sundays and at weekday gatherings. For hours each day he studied the Bible and wrote down the verses and chapters in English.

The longer Tyndale stayed in London and the more he talked to men who had been traveling in Europe, the more he came to understand that there was going to be a real struggle between those who wanted freedom of religion, like Luther, and those who wanted to follow the pope's rules and laws.

"I'd better get out of England," decided William Tyndale. "The bishop isn't the only one here who might make things very hard for me."

So in May of 1524, you might have seen a young man, tightly wrapped up in a long cloak, hanging to the railing of a sailing vessel that was carrying him across the stormy English channel to a land new and strange to him, to the city of Hamburg in Germany.

"I wonder," thought young Tyndale, "how it would be to visit Martin Luther?" His heart beat just a bit harder at the thought of visiting that champion of religious freedom and of seeing the man around whose head a storm of discussion raged.

No one quite knows whether Tyndale spent the next year with Luther or not. Some of his friends seem to have been sure that he did some of his translating in the very town where Luther was living. Whether he did or not, we do not know. It seems probable that he visited and talked with the great man and was made stronger and more full of courage by knowing him.

All during that year he worked on his translation of the New Testament. At last it was done and ready to be printed. Tyndale went to Cologne. There in that beautiful German city lived the most famous printers of that day, such as Peter Quental.

"Will you print me three thousand copies of the New Testament in English?" asked William Tyndale of Peter Quental.

"Gladly," said Quental, and the work began.

Tyndale didn't know that Quental was at that very time printing a book for John Cochlaeus, who hated Luther and his works with all his heart.

One day when John Cochlaeus had come to see how his book was getting along, he heard the printers talking and laughing.

"Ha!" they said. "Won't the king of England tear his beard with rage!" They doubled up with laughter. "Here we are printing a translation of the New Testament in English, which is a thing he would never allow. Soon it will be shipped into England, and all the pious Englishmen will become Lutherans!"

Cochlaeus could hardly believe his ears. An English translation of the New Testament being printed in Cologne! He hurried over to the printers and began to ask them questions. But they would give him no information. More than one of them knew how Cochlaeus felt toward the translations of the Bible by Luther.

Cochlaeus did not despair. He invited the men to the tavern and treated them to drink after drink. "That will loosen their tight tongues," he growled to himself.

Loosen them the liquor did! Cochlaeus found out every single thing he wanted to know about William Tyndale's translation. He shut his lips to a thin, hard line and went to his lodging and wrote a letter to the rulers of the great city of Cologne, telling what he had learned.

The rulers wrote to England. The leading clergymen were furious. Plans were made to destroy Tyndale's translation.

But Tyndale received a warning of what was to happen. He and his friend William Roye rushed to the printers' shop. They snatched up the precious handwritten sheets of the translation and wrapped them as carefully as they could in their haste. They fled from the city of Cologne and went to Worms. Once more a printer was engaged. The pages were set in type. The presses began to work.

This time the printing was finished without interference and the task of smuggling the copies into England had to be faced.

It was simple at first to pack the printed books in with bales of cloth and other articles being sent to England, for in that way they could go to many, many towns and homes.

People received them eagerly.

To the horror and indignation of the king and of the Bishop of London and of the other high church officials, the thing they had done all in their power to prevent had happened. The New Testament in English was actually being put into people's hands and being read by them. The knowledge made the church officials furious.

When the officials finally got hold of a copy, they were angrier than ever, and not altogether without cause. For Tyndale had printed comments in the margins of his New Testament. Some of the comments were about the clergymen and the pope and were anything but complimentary! These remarks by Tyndale, printed there in the margin for everyone to read, were simply the last straw.

"Burn them!" shouted the bishop. "Burn every last one of the New Testaments that you can find!"

And burn them they did! Sometimes they burned just a few. But often they made a great bonfire of all the books that the church didn't like.

Attempts were made to seize Tyndale at Worms, but he escaped to Marburg. In 1529 he went to Antwerp.

One day the Bishop of London was talking to a merchant named Mr. Packington. "When you are over in Antwerp, hunt me out those New Testaments," he begged. "Buy them for whatever they cost you, and I will pay you," he urged.

Packington went to Antwerp on his next trip and hunted up William Tyndale. "How about selling some of the Testaments at a good price?" he asked.

"To whom?"

"To the Bishop of London," said Packington with a quick wink of the eye.

Tyndale thought it over. The Bishop of London would pay a good price to get hold of hundreds of Testaments to burn. With the money Tyndale could print more hundreds and just that many more people would be able to own and read them.

One day a little later, Packington went to the Bishop of London with a mule loaded with the Testaments. He took his pay for them and received the bishop's thanks with a solemn face. But he laughed heartily when on his next trip to the continent he turned the money over to William Tyndale. With it Tyndale printed more copies of the New Testament than Packington had sold to the bishop.

The years slipped by, and William Tyndale printed more and more Testaments. All the while he worked at translating the Old Testament.

One day, in 1535, a man who had pretended to be a friend of Tyndale invited him to go with him out from the safe house where he was living in Antwerp. Tyndale gladly went with the man. But the man was really an enemy. He led Tyndale directly to an armed guard who threw him into prison.

After a while Tyndale was allowed a candle in the evening, so that he might not have to sit alone for the long hours in the darkness. He was even allowed to have his Hebrew Bible, grammar, and dictionary.

Day after day in his lonely prison cell Tyndale worked, translating the chapters of the Old Testament.

Months passed. A year went by.

Nothing his friends could do secured his release. The angry haters of Luther and of a Bible that could be read by the people were too strong.

And then one day Tyndale was led out and strangled at the stake, and his body was burned.

But even when he knew he was to die, Tyndale was not afraid. He was glad—glad that he had given his life to translating the Bible into English and smuggling the copies to

England. He knew that just one thing was needed to complete his work. And before he died he prayed one fervent prayer: "Lord, open the king of England's eyes!" He felt sure that if the king could come to see how important it was that people should have the Bible in English, he would order copies printed.

It was only a year after that the king changed his mind about the Bible. "It is right to have the Bible in English," said King Henry VIII. The friends of Tyndale rejoiced. They knew that nothing would have pleased him more than to know that no longer did Bibles need to be smuggled into the land, and that his work had made it easier for the common people to have the Bible in their own language.

3: Reading the Great Bible

England (after 1536)

Kɪɴɢ ʜᴇɴʀʏ ᴠɪɪɪ rubbed his forehead fretfully. Thomas Cromwell had been talking to him again about the need for an English Bible.

"There is too much quarreling about the Bible," Cromwell had said. "Some want to use Tyndale's version and some like Thomas Matthew's. Still others say that the new Bible of Miles Coverdale is the best. The king should say which Bible is the best to use. The king should order that an English Bible be printed for the people of England. It should be placed in every parish church for the people to read."

Cromwell had talked until King Henry had shown that he was weary of the subject. Then he had withdrawn, for in those days a king's counselor did not linger when his royal master showed displeasure.

During the next few weeks, Henry thought often of Cromwell's words. Finally he said to himself as he stroked his silky beard, "It is a good idea and I will do it."

"After all," muttered Henry, "I am now the head of the Church in England and I can order a Bible printed if I wish!" He shouted, "Send me Thomas Cromwell!"

When Thomas Cromwell came striding into the room, the king waved his hand. "Have a new Bible printed in English," said he, as if he had thought of the idea, all by himself.

Thomas Cromwell bowed and went smilingly away. A little later he talked to Miles Coverdale, who had had printed the first entire Bible in the English language. "Will you prepare the text?" he asked.

Miles Coverdale agreed. He could use the translation he had already made.

"It would be well to have it printed in Paris," suggested Cromwell. "The best presses are there. I can assure you," he added grimly, "that the king will not be content with anything but the very best."

Miles Coverdale set to work.

After a while Coverdale had the first part of the copy ready. As fast as his pages were prepared, the presses of Paris ran them off. While the first pages were in the presses, printers worked busily setting up other pages in type. The Bible that the king had ordered printed would soon be ready. Some of its pages were sent over to England.

But after a while Cromwell became uneasy. There was danger in Europe. Those who did not want the common people to have the Bible were struggling to suppress it. Cromwell knew that these enemies might suddenly come with armed men, seize and burn the presses, the paper, the printed pages, and the copy.

Some pages actually had been seized and sold to a hatter by the enemies. Cromwell gave orders to have the materials rushed to England. "Here," said he with his tight-lipped smile, "we can work without interruption!"

Coverdale and an English printer brought the type, the paper, and the printers to England and the work went on.

At last, in 1539, the Bibles were printed. They were huge. People called the edition "The Great Bible" because it was so big.

"Now that it is printed," said King Henry, "it must be read!"

He issued a proclamation. The proclamation said that the Bible was to be read in the churches. And it added that three or four copies of the Bible were to be placed on reading desks in various parts of the larger churches, so that people who wished to do so might go in and read for themselves.

What Henry VIII ordered was usually done in a hurry.

It was not long before the worshipers going into the great churches and cathedrals of England found reading desks set here and there. And on each desk lay one of the beautiful new Great Bibles. Each Bible was firmly chained to its desk, so that no one might carry it off.

Now in those days, reading was not as usual as it is today. Only a few people could read and there were few books. Most people who could read did so out loud. So when a merchant stopped in front of the Great Bible, he would turn the pages till he came to something that interested him and then he would read aloud. Those around him, particularly if they themselves could not read, listened with interest and attention.

After a while, when the merchant was gone, a scholar might come. And he, too, turning the thick pages, would begin to read out loud.

Perhaps a schoolboy, or a nobleman's daughter, or a clerk from some store might happen in. And each was delighted to find the Bible and to read. Perhaps some read louder than was necessary, so that everyone within hearing might say, "Ah, there is someone who knows how to read!" and look with admiration at that person. Who knows?

At any rate, the ones who read aloud from the new treasure of England seemed not to be bothered by the fact that sometimes a service was going on. So it often happened that right in the middle of a sermon, a loud voice would begin reading from the Psalms. Or perhaps one voice would rise, shouting the Ten Commandments from one side of the church, while another as loudly read the Beatitudes from the other side. And the attention of the congregation would be sadly distracted from the words of the preacher who was addressing them.

So for a while there was confusion during the church services. A rule had to be made—"Do not read aloud when services are going on." When there was no service those who wished to do so might read aloud from the Bibles placed so handily for their use.

King Henry VIII smiled as he stroked his beard. Little did he know how very soon the chained Bibles were to be snatched from the reading desks and the reading of the Bible by the people forbidden! For when his daughter Mary ruled after him, she took away the English Bibles from the churches.

But then, neither could he know that after a time the custom he had started would be established once more and a free people would have freedom to read, whenever and however they pleased, the words of the Bible—their guide and their light upon the pathway to God.

4: The Church That Had No Bible

India (1806)

PALM trees stood out against a blue, blue sky, with wind whipping their branches. It was a hot wind, and people stayed as close inside their houses as they could.

"I knew it was hot in India, but never had I imagined such heat as this!" muttered Mr. Buchanan, the newly arrived chaplain for the East India Company.

"It will be hotter before the rains break," said those who had been living longer in that sun-drenched land. "Do you want to ship back to England? There's a vessel due to sail next week."

Mr. Buchanan sighed. There could be no question about his going back to green, cool England. He had work to do here and he intended to do it.

The months rolled by and Mr. Buchanan became more used to the climate. He learned something of the language and became interested in the people of the west coast of India.

Then he discovered something that interested him more than anything he had yet come across. He found that there were some Indian Christian churches in Travancore that were very old. He had always thought that India was a country with no Christian churches except those started by modern missionaries.

The people in these churches were called St. Thomas Christians. Priests led their services and gave the people instruction.

"But India has not been a Christian land. It is a pagan land!" cried puzzled Mr. Buchanan.

"Ah, yes. Just the same, churches have existed here on the west coast of India ever since the days when St. Thomas himself came and preached to our ancestors," the St. Thomas Christians proudly told him. "Our church is older than almost any other."

Mr. Buchanan was shown their buildings. On them were carved writings. People who knew about such things told Mr. Buchanan that those carvings were certainly more than a thousand years old. Some of the crosses on the buildings were just as old.

"If the buildings are that old," thought Mr. Buchanan, "the church itself must be still older. It must have been started hundreds of years before the buildings that are here today. I wonder! I wonder! Could Thomas, the disciple who followed Jesus up and down the dusty roads of Judea and Galilee, really have come to India? Is it possible that he walked the dusty roads of this land so far from his own country and preached the wonderful message of God's love to the people of India?"

"No one knows. But we have always been called the St. Thomas Christians, and we ourselves believe that St. Thomas did come. Our church goes back further than any written record," said those he questioned.

Mr. Buchanan began to find out more about the churches. Somehow they did not seem to be getting along very well. The churches were not growing. The people were not living as though they knew the Christian teachings.

One day Mr. Buchanan was talking to the priests. "Do you have a Bible?" he asked.

"Oh, yes," they smiled. "We have copies of the Bible. They exist. But they are written in a language called Syriac. None of the people speak or read or understand that language here. We read from the Syriac Bible sometimes in the church service. But only the priests understand! So it is really not much use reading."

"I should think not!" said Mr. Buchanan to himself. "How

can a church exist at all without God's Word in the hearts of its people?"

Out loud he asked, "Why don't you translate it so that the people can understand it?"

"Translate it!" The priests seemed surprised. They seemed even a little shocked. "You mean translate the Bible? Put the Holy Scriptures into a language different from the Syriac? Why we never heard of a Bible in the language that the common people understand!"

Mr. Buchanan took out his copy of the Bible. "Here, look at this." They examined it. "This is the Bible translated into my language, the language of the common people of England. Your people should have the Bible translated into their language."

"Into Malayalam? Into the language of Travancore?"

"Certainly. That is what the people speak, isn't it?"

It took some time to persuade the priests. They had thought of the Bible as something rather magical, to be opened with reverence and ceremony and read in its ancient syllables by one of the few who could do so. They had thought of it as something to be heard with the ears but not as something to be understood by the mind.

Mr. Buchanan kept on with his argument. At last he won.

"We will do it," the priests agreed. "We will begin with the four Gospels, the story of the life of our Lord upon the earth."

So the priests sat down with the old, old Syriac version before them which only they understood. They began the long, hard task of translating the four Gospels. Sentence by sentence, chapter by chapter, book by book, the work was done. When the Gospels were all written out in the everyday speech of the people of Travancore, the priests took the manuscript to Bombay. There were the presses on which it could be printed. Mr. Buchanan was in Bombay and he agreed to arrange for the printing and to oversee it.

In 1811 Mr. Buchanan saw the four Gospels printed, only five years after he had first found out about the church with the Bible in Syriac.

What a day it was when the printed copies went back to Travancore! What a day when the priests stood up in church and read to the people in their own language about Jesus and his teachings!

"This is new!" cried the people. "This is real!"

They and their priests began to compare the teachings and practices of their church with what the New Testament said.

"We must change our ways," they decided. "We must follow the teachings of Jesus and not just the old traditions."

Thus there came about a change in the old, old church. So great were the changes that the church adopted a new name for itself, taken from the idea that its members were St. Thomas Christians. It is now called the Mar Thoma Church, in memory of St. Thomas, who first brought the teachings of Jesus to the shores of India. The church is guided now by those same teachings read from the Bible, and it has become eager to give the message of the gospel to others.

The Bible is used in the services now, and there are copies in the homes of the people. "We each like to have our own copy of God's Word," the people say. "How can we know how God wants us to live unless we read the teachings of the Bible?"

So the church that had no Bible has become a church that is living by the Bible. It has changed and become wide-awake and alive. It is a blessing to its members and to the people around who still have not come to be followers of Jesus.

5: Biscuits Into Bibles

New Hebrides (1848-1872)

LAND!" bellowed the lookout far up in the crow's nest. His voice came down to the deck of the sturdy oaken ship that was ploughing its way through the blue waters of the Pacific.

"Land!" he shouted once again.

No one had waited for the second call. Every man on the ship had rushed to catch a glimpse of the sight that they had longed to see. The sailors sprang up among the billowing white sails to get a better look. The few passengers hurried to the prow.

Among them was John Geddie.

He was eager to see land. It was going to be different from anything that he had ever seen in all his life. John was from the province of Nova Scotia in Canada. The waves of the Atlantic Ocean beat upon the shores of his land. Dark firs and pines, snow and ice, and short, sweet summer were what he had always known.

Now he had come to live in the South Sea Islands. He was to carry the gospel message to the people of the New Hebrides Islands. That is, he was to carry to them the gospel message if he escaped being eaten by cannibals.

It was some hours after sighting land that they came close enough to the first island for John to see it clearly. Then he gazed and gazed. Like green emeralds on the blue ocean lay the islands. Great palm trees rose from them. White sand fringed them.

The island of Aneityum, on which John landed, was friendly to visitors and traders. There was no danger there of his being eaten to make a cannibal feast.

He was even able to get the use of a native house, and he

found the dark-skinned, dark-eyed islanders willing to have him live among them, even though they were not particularly interested in the idea of his teaching them about God.

"We have our own gods," said one to another, "and why should we care about the god of a bleached-out person like this stranger?"

John stood on the beach with the crowd of dusky-skinned men, women, and children to watch the ship sail off. All around him the people were laughing and talking to one another. Not one word could John understand.

"I'll have to learn their language," he said to himself. "That's the first thing." He began to listen to the sound and the swing of their sentences while his eyes followed the white sails getting smaller and smaller in the distance until they were gone.

The island men who traded with the ships that came knew enough English to help John get the things he actually needed. But the English words in which the islanders offered arrowroot for sale and in which they asked for the few articles they could afford to buy from the ship were not those that could be used in telling the people about God's love. Nor did they have anything much to do with telling the story of Jesus.

"I don't want to teach the islanders English," said John to himself, "so that they can read an English Bible and listen to Christian teaching in English. I want to learn the Aneityum language that they speak, so that when I tell a Bible story the oldest grandmother and the littlest child will understand it. I want to learn to speak so well and so exactly that the people will think it is one of themselves who is talking."

Very soon John had learned a great many words of the island language. But he wanted to do better than that. He wanted to have the islanders say certain words over and over and over, so slowly that he could find out exactly where he should put his tongue and how he should hold his lips to make each sound correctly. "Thistle," said John to himself, noticing that to make the "th" sound in English, he had to put his tongue under and against his upper teeth with his lips open. Then he said "what," and smiled as he found he must draw his lips up into a circle and almost blow through them.

"I wonder," said he, "whether the sounds of the language I'm trying to learn are made in such different ways. I must get help from the people of the islands."

Now the islanders were glad enough to tell John words for objects around them. But they thought it silly and undignified to say a word over and over, very slowly, while John tried to see just how their lips and their tongues and their teeth were held.

So they stalked away offended, and John began to think he would never get the language sounds correctly and exactly. And unless he did, he could not invent a way to write them down.

One day John was nibbling at some hardtack. It was the stiff, tough ship's biscuit that was used instead of bread on long voyages because it kept so well. At first John had refused to eat hardtack, but after a while he came to like the dry, salty flavor and to enjoy nibbling at a biscuit. The ship's captain had left a box of the hardtack with him to help out with his food.

One man who had been helping John with words and had stalked off in disgust came sauntering by. Almost without thinking, John tossed him a bit of hardtack. "Have a biscuit!" said John in English.

His helper bit cautiously into it. Then he tried again. Soon he was nibbling around the edges, delighted with the taste. Never had he eaten anything just like this.

It wasn't long before his hand was stretched out for another.

John had an idea.

"I'll trade you!" said John.

And trade him he did. But what he got in return was not trade goods. It was language sounds.

Before long other men found out that the strange foreign food was to be had for nothing more than making silly repetitions of certain sounds in front of the odd person who was trying to learn their language. There was no lack of helpers now, willing to repeat as often as necessary any word that John had a notion to hear.

Biscuit after biscuit was handed over to the islanders. One after another the sounds of the language became clear and easy for John to repeat.

Meanwhile he was working out an alphabet for the many sounds. And he was putting the words of the language into writing.

It was not long before John was able to talk to the people about God. He began to tell them the story of Jesus.

The story he told them was from the Book of *Mark*. As he worked out the words and told the story, he wrote it down. Then he took his Bible and wrote down more exactly the very words of the Gospel of *Mark*.

The islanders had come to know John well before that was finished. They had grown to love and trust him. Many was the fishing expedition on which they took him. He visited their fields of arrowroot and saw how they grew the crop and got it ready to sell to the ships that came to buy it. He saw their worship and heard the legends and the stories of their island gods. He found out the customs of their lives and how they lived.

Patiently he taught them, and in time many of them became Christians.

Besides his teaching John spent part of each day working on the translation of the Bible, starting with the Gospel of *Mark*. After it was finished, he sent it to Sydney to be printed. Then he went on with the translation of the New Testament.

When the little printed Gospels of *Mark* arrived back on the island, the people were delighted. Some of them could already read a few words. Most of them could read none. John Geddie set to work to teach them.

All the while he was working away at his translation. When the Gospel of *Matthew* was finished it was printed on a little press that John had bought for use on the island.

In time the whole New Testament was finished.

"Now," said John joyfully to his island friends, "we must have the New Testament printed."

John realized that it would take a lot of money. It could not be done on the little press of the island.

John called the chief men of the island together.

"We now have the New Testament in your language," said he.

"True! And it is a very wonderful thing that it should be so," answered the oldest leader.

"The next thing is to have many copies made on a machine."

The men waited for him to continue.

"That takes money."

No one said a word.

"I have no money," said John Geddie sadly.

"Neither have we," said the chief men.

There was silence for a while. John said, "Your people grow arrowroot for sale to the ships that pass. Would they be willing to set aside one-tenth of their crop and sell it separately? Would they be willing to give the money they received for that one-tenth toward printing the Bible?"

The chief men went away and talked to the people.

The people were willing. Each one said he would set aside one-tenth of his crop.

So they did. And when that one-tenth was harvested and sold the money came to two thousand dollars!

John sent his precious copy of the New Testament in the language of the islanders, and with it the money, to a faraway place where the printing could be done.

Months passed and no word of the printing came to the island. Then one day a passing ship unloaded some bundles for John Geddie. They held the long-awaited Testaments.

Each family received one and there were some left over. A great many of the people still could not read.

"We'll have everyone learn!" said John.

So a contest was held. Prizes were offered to those who could read best from the New Testaments.

How hard the islanders worked! More than two thousand of them began to read.

Two thousand people were reading the Testaments every day. And the rest of the people on that island were listening to the reading and to the teaching. John Geddie was a busy man. He was now at work on the translation of the Old Testament. By 1872 most of it was done.

Twenty-four years had gone by since John Geddie first heard that shout of "Land!" from the crow's nest of the ship that was bringing him to the island. And in that twenty-fourth year, John Geddie died.

"He has left us for the heavenly home," said his sorrowing islanders. And they put up a tablet in the biggest church on the island. On it were these words:

> "When he landed in 1848
> There were no Christians here;
> And when he left in 1872
> There were no heathen."

6: In an Unknown Tongue

Canada (1855-1864)

JOHN WOLSEY shivered as he waded out of the icy stream that came tumbling down from the high slopes of the Canadian Rockies. The two scantily clad Indians who were his guides waited scornfully while he put on his clothing. He had taken it off and carried it, bound securely to his shoulders, across that slippery riverbed.

His shoes were soaked. He had had to choose between getting them wet and cutting his feet on the sharp rocks of the riverbed. His handknit wool socks felt warm to his numbed feet, but it was hard getting the wet shoes back on over them.

He smiled wryly. He would warm up again, soon enough, trying to keep up the pace of his Indian companions. If he had understood them aright, they would reach, sometime during the afternoon, the tepees of the tribe they were seeking.

John Wolsey's heart beat a little faster. There was always the chance, when he visited a tribe for the first time, that it would be his last visit to anyone. So far he had succeeded in making friends with the chiefs and no harm had come to him. But there was always the possibility that things would go wrong in the end. Then his scalplock would adorn the outfit of some gallant brave and his dead body would be thrown out for wild animals to devour.

He stumbled along the rocky trail till he warmed up, and then moved almost as quickly and quietly as the Indians. He was learning, on these long, wild trips, to make the most of his strength.

A sudden stop made him look up.

The younger guide was gazing ahead and a little to one side. A thin column of smoke rose into the air.

"My people!" said the young warrior. "Wait here."

John Wolsey did not question the order. The young man would go forward and tell of the coming of the Pale Face, and win him, at least, a hearing. Meantime the older warrior guarded the traveler, lest a wandering hunter of the camp should come by and think him fair game.

It was almost an hour before John's young companion returned, slipping noiselessly among the evergreens that crowded one another over these foothills of the mighty range.

He motioned to the travelers. "The chief will receive you," he said briefly.

There was no need for him to say more. John had been working hard since he came, so few months ago, among these Crees. He knew a few words of their language now and had learned to understand the simple directions of his guides. But he still could not follow their conversation with one another and he could say nothing of importance to them, beyond that which covered the needs of the day.

The chief and his braves scowled as John Wolsey came into the camp. What could a Pale Face be wanting with them? And he carried no great pack of presents either!

John Wolsey walked steadily toward the group. Then he stopped and extended both hands. "Friends!" he said.

Then he motioned to the older guide. "Tell them," he said.

The older man spoke. He had seen John Wolsey visit other strange tribes and he knew what happened on those visits.

"This Pale Face travels with no weapons," said he. "He carries, instead, O Chief, a bundle of white sheets, thinner than birch bark, tougher than leaves. On them are marks as if twigs burned to charcoal had been drawn across them. This he takes, and holding it in his hand he fastens his eyes upon it."

The chief bent forward to listen. The braves drew in a long breath. What was this strange thing that the Pale Face did?

The guide went on. "Then, O Chief, by some magic that I do not understand, this Pale Face who cannot speak our language, opens his mouth, and the words of our tongue come from his lips. Tales that no one of our people has ever heard before come roundly forth from his mouth. And the teachings are about a Great Spirit who is like a loving father."

"Magic!" whispered the women and children, hidden behind the deerskins at the doors of the tepees. "Surely he is a powerful one, this Pale Face."

"Magic?" questioned the chief. "Does he make spells and incantations?"

"Not so," said the guide. "He is like any other Pale Face. Yet, not quite like, for although he is ignorant and cannot follow a forest trail as plain as a hand leading him, he endures with fortitude. And anger never governs him. Nor does he complain when game is scarce and we must needs travel without food."

"And what does he want of us? He is far, far from his own people," said the chief suspiciously.

"He wants to sit around the fire when the camp is quiet after the day's hunt and men's hunger is stilled by food. He will unfasten his pack and bring out the white pieces with the black marks upon them, and then open his lips and say the words that the magic guides him to speak. That is all that he wishes, O Chief."

The chief considered. He did not care for the Pale Faces. Only last moon, two trappers who had come blundering along had lost their scalps. He did not like the Pale Faces with their firewater that made the young braves boastful and foolish.

But this man—somehow he looked different. He stood firmly among them, with no trace of fear upon his face— only a great friendliness.

"Let him stay. Tell the women to set up a tepee for him. But let him be guarded. It may be a trick," said the wily chief.

Well within the lines of the other tepees, a small one was pitched for John Wolsey. He unpacked his blanket and his one change of clothing. From the very center of the pack, wrapped in soft doeskin, he took those thin white sheets of which the guide had spoken.

He turned the little bundle of paper sheets over in his hands and looked at the letters on them. He turned the pages slowly, deciding from the references just what he would read to these Indians who had never, in all their lives, heard one word from the Bible.

Then John Wolsey smiled to himself, because he himself could not understand more than a word here and there of what he was going to read.

"I'd not have thought it!" he murmured. "To come into a camp of Indians whose language I do not know and to read to them the message of the gospel with words I do not understand!" He looked at the pages again.

"Surely," he half-whispered, "surely God himself guided James Evans[1] to invent this writing for the Cree tongue, for it is so simple that I, who do not know that language, can read its sounds. And the sounds carry its meaning to the ears that listen."

Then he knelt there in his little tepee and prayed. He prayed that he might be guided to choose the right passage from the pages of the Bible that he carried. He prayed that the hearts of the Indians might be opened to hear the message of God's love. Most of all he prayed that he might always

[1] See page 174 for the Cree alphabet invented by James Evans.

behave with such friendliness, love, and courage that the wild Indian braves might want to know more of the Great Spirit whom he worshiped.

The slow twilight drew to a close. The evening meal was over. The campfire blazed, throwing leaping shadows of squaw and brave against the rock walls of the lonely valley in which the camp was set.

John Wolsey sat calmly waiting. At last the chief motioned to him and he strode forward. He knelt so the flickering flame lighted up the pages in his hand.

He read, slowly and clearly, although the sounds that came from his lips had no meaning to his ears.

The chief and the braves stared motionless at first. And then, of a sudden, they realized that the sounds coming from the lips of the Pale Face were speaking to them in words they could understand.

" 'In the beginning the Great Spirit created the heavens and the earth—' " and on through the story of Creation.

John Wolsey turned to another sheet.

" 'The Great Spirit so loved the world that he sent his only beloved Son—' "

There was no sound but the crackling of the wood in the fire and the stir of a breeze in the tops of the evergreens.

Again John Wolsey took a new sheet. He read of Jesus as he taught and healed, and ministered to the needy.

The fire died down to embers, but no one moved hand or foot. A baby whimpered in its mother's arms and she soothed it quickly, yet did not stop listening.

Then John Wolsey spoke haltingly the few words of Cree that he had memorized. The words told the Indians that God, the Great Spirit, loved them as he loved all his other children. They said to the Indians that God wanted them to love him and live as his children, walking in the trail that had been marked by the Lord Jesus Christ.

There was silence by the campfire. At last the chief spoke. "It is a strange story," he said. "Never has anyone come to us with such a story. Is there more to be told?" He pointed to the pages.

John Wolsey motioned to his guide. The older brave spoke. "Again and again he makes his lips speak, gazing always at the sheets he holds in his hands, for two nights, for three nights, for four nights. And then, unless the chief asks him to spend more nights by his campfire, he goes on," added the older guide.

"Goes on where?"

The young brave spoke. "From here, O Chief-of-My-People, he returns to his own place. Many days' journey have we come, stopping for two days, for three days, for four days at the tepees of our people wherever we found them. When it is your wish to send him away, I have given my word to guide him back to his own people."

"Good." The chief rose swiftly. "Tomorrow night we will hear these words again. They are strange—strange."

The braves leaped to their feet. Someone covered the coals with ashes. The moon just looking down into the valley saw only dark figures slipping into their tepees.

Rolled in his blanket, John Wolsey lay for a few moments with open eyes. He was content. He was more than content, for as he had read that evening, sounding forth the syllables from the black letters that lay before him, he had seen faces alight with interest. "Some day, please God," murmured John Wolsey drowsily, "the Cree people will know how to read, and missionary men and women who know their speech will come among them, and bring them the whole Bible of whose pages I have so few." And thinking of that day, he fell asleep, unafraid in the midst of a tribe whose first white friend he was.

7: When the "Morning Star" Sailed

Gilbert Islands (1856-1894)

THE *Morning Star* set her sails to the wind and slipped out of old Boston Harbor. She was a special kind of vessel—a missionary ship. The children of the Congregational churches had her for their very own ship, to carry missionaries to far-off islands and to visit them and carry supplies to them from time to time.

On the rough dock there were a group of people whose lips moved silently in prayer as the good ship sailed farther and farther from them. They prayed for those on board for a safe voyage first, and for their welfare in the cannibal islands of the South Seas after their journey was over.

On board, the passengers felt a strange thrill. They were leaving home and country and friends, perhaps never to see them again. Like Paul, they were going to strange places and among unfriendly people. Like him, they had just one purpose in mind and that was to carry the gospel to the islands of the South Seas.

Young Hiram Bingham, just twenty-five years old, and his wife, who was younger, stood together by the ship's rail. They had all the courage of their ancestors who had come to America, then an unknown land. Now they themselves were going to an unknown country and they hoped to make it a Christian land before they died.

On sailed the ship. Far to the south it went, till it came to the tip of South America. Around the tip it went, and then turned north and west. On and on and on! Finally it came to a group of islands that we now call Hawaii.

There Hiram Bingham and his wife landed. They were going to stay there for a few months before going on.

Hiram was no stranger to the Hawaiian Islands. He had been born there and he loved the place. His father had gone there as a missionary. Hiram had watched his father translate the Bible into the Hawaiian language. He had even done his small share to help by carrying pages to the printer.

At last the time came to go on from Hawaii. The *Morning Star*, which spent its time sailing from one missionary outpost to another, was ready to set out for the Gilbert Islands. Those islands were a thousand miles to the southwest of Hawaii. They lay like tiny jewels in the vast Pacific. It was to one of them that Hiram and his wife were to go. Across the thousand miles of ocean the ship sailed steadily with her passengers.

Once more the gallant little *Morning Star* came to anchor. But this time it was within the reef of a lagoon on the island of Apaiang. Hiram Bingham and his wife were ready to disembark. Their few possessions were lowered and taken to the beach in the ship's rowboat.

The shores were lined with dark-skinned natives. Their faces were not unfriendly, for another missionary couple had visited them during the previous year. The king was willing to have Hiram come because he realized that the missionary people were different from the crews of the trading boats who so often in those days carried off strong young boys to sell into slavery. His people were ready to murder the crews of such boats without any hesitation, but the missionaries had made a different impression.

Along with their chests, the *Morning Star* unloaded materials for building a simple house in which Hiram and his wife could live.

Then the sails were hoisted. The little ship slipped quietly out from behind the reef, and the two young people were left on an island a thousand miles from Hawaii. They were surrounded by other little islands on which lived hostile people. They did not know whether, when the *Morning Star* came again next year, they would be there to welcome it or not.

Now came the business of learning the language spoken by the people of the Gilbert Islands. There was just one way to do it. Hiram would point to an object. An islander would give the name for it in his language. Hiram would repeat the word the islander said. Then he would point to something else and get its name. That word would be repeated. He would hear a mother shout to her child and the child would reply and come running. He wondered whether the mother had said, "Dinner!" or "Bad boy, come here!" or "Quick, I need help!"

That was something to guess at. But by listening and watching and questioning, Hiram and his wife learned more and more words. They learned phrases and even sentences.

But how were the words to be put into writing? Hiram and his wife had to make an alphabet. Then they could put into writing the new words and phrases they had learned.

They began to try to find out words for the ideas in the Gospel of *Matthew* and to translate that book of the Bible. It helped a lot for Hiram to know how his father had gone about the job in Hawaii. He knew what mistakes not to make, and some of the short cuts. But just the same it took a long time.

At last twelve chapters of the Gospel were done. A visiting sailing ship carried the manuscript back across a thousand miles of ocean to Hawaii. There the chapters were printed. It took months, but oh, what a thrill it was to Hiram and his wife when another vessel came out of its way to bring those printed pages to Apaiang!

Meanwhile Hiram and his wife had been teaching the people as well as learning the language. They had helpers now from among the people of the island. Hiram had even visited some of the near-by unfriendly islands and talked to their people about the message of Jesus. While the first chapters were being printed he had gone on translating the rest of the Gospel of *Matthew*.

It was not too long before the whole Gospel of *Matthew* had been sent to Hawaii for printing. More months went by. Then one day, white sails appeared on the horizon, and a ship laid its course straight for Apaiang! Every person was down on the beach to meet it, for the Christians of the little island were as eager to see the printed Gospel as were the Binghams. They supposed, of course, that the ship was bringing it.

But no! The ship brought a message instead, and a disappointing one. The printers of Hawaii were too busy to publish the book. Instead, they had what they thought was a brilliant idea. They sent the manuscript back. Along with it they sent a little printing press in a box with type and ink and paper. "Print the Gospel yourselves!" they wrote. "And you can print other things, too, and not have to wait so long for them."

Hiram stared at the box. He didn't know one single thing about printing presses. He felt very gloomy.

After the visiting ship was gone, Hiram and his wife unpacked the press. But they could not figure out how it worked and there was nothing they could do about it. They would have to wait until another ship came and send the manuscript of *Matthew* once more to Hawaii to be printed. They felt so disappointed that they could hardly speak to each other about the press.

One morning two days later, a small boy shouted loudly to Hiram, "Quick! Quick! A boat is coming!"

Hiram and his wife rushed out of their house. They could hardly believe their eyes. There across the little lagoon that was sheltered from the rolling waves of the ocean, a tiny rowboat was being pulled toward them.

They rushed down to the beach.

The weary rowers looked as astonished as Hiram. "Where's your ship?" shouted Hiram.

"Wrecked and gone down in the storm," answered the men, who, he could see now, were sailors. "We four are all who are saved. We landed on another island and heard that here we could get a ship that would take us home."

The shipwrecked men were as thankful as they were astonished to find a missionary and his wife and a Christian group of people on the island. They ate eagerly the food that was prepared for them. They needed sleep and rest almost as much as food.

As soon as they had recovered from their perilous experience, the four men wandered around the island, giving a hand with whatever Hiram set them to doing. One of them, whose name was Hotchkiss, came upon the printing press.

"What's this!" he exclaimed. "Do you print things here on this island?"

"No," and Hiram sadly explained what had happened.

Hotchkiss smiled broadly. "I'm a printer," said he, "and in no time at all I'll have this little beauty of a hand press working. Give me what it is you want printed. I'll do it, and show you how, too," he added.

Hiram was overjoyed. "It is God himself who sent you," said he.

Busy days followed. Hotchkiss set up the press. When a sailing vessel came by and took away the other shipwrecked men, he stayed to finish the printing and to teach Hiram and his islanders the art of managing the press.

So there came into the hands of the islanders of Apaiang the whole book of *Matthew* in their own language. And after that the Gospel of *John,* and the *Epistle to the Ephesians.* More could not be printed then, for there was only a small amount of paper. But Hiram and his wife rejoiced every time they saw one of those precious copies in the hands of an earnestly reading islander.

The Bible had come to the Gilbert Islands.

The years went by, and all the people in the Gilbert Islands became Christians. The year 1892 is one to remember, for in that year Hiram Bingham finished the translation of the whole Bible.

He did not try to print it on the island. The manuscript was sent to New York, to the American Bible Society, and they printed it. Hiram and his wife went to New York for the reading of the proofs.

The Bible was printed in 1893.

The precious plates, from which the printing is done when new copies are needed, lie in the fireproof vault of the American Bible Society's building in New York. They are the only plates of the Bible in Gilbertese in all the world, and no one wants to risk their getting destroyed.

So, today when Gilbertese Bibles are needed, a message goes from the islands to New York. The Bibles are packed and taken to a ship. Soon they are on their way across the rolling ocean waves to the islands where long years ago the *Morning Star* dropped anchor. And on those islands, where Hiram Bingham and his wife lived and worked so bravely, a Christian people today reads in its own language the message of God's love.

8: The Bible Rides the Western Plains

United States (1860)

Young Charles slipped from his horse's back as the little company of riders came to a stop below the crest of the hill. Up over the hill ahead of them went the faint trail.

"Wait here!" Charles ordered curtly, and the others waited. They did not mind, because they understood the reason. Again and again as Charles had guided them across the almost trackless plain the same thing had happened. Charles was taking no chances on meeting Apache warriors, or on riding into a nest of bandits with the men he was convoying across the western plains. Not for nothing was he known as one of the keenest and the toughest of the young plainsmen. Folk felt safe if Charles Martin undertook to guide them where they wanted to go.

Charles moved silently up the hillside. Stooping behind a shrubby tree near the crest, he crept forward. A moment later he was gone from sight. Many a time had he spied out the land from beneath the cover of a stunted bit of growth along the lonely trail.

Presently he strode down the slope and swung into his saddle. "Plains clear as far as the eye can see," he said briefly. The horses started and the long journey across the plains continued.

That night the riders camped in an arroyo, a gulley cut by the winter floods, below the level of the plain they were crossing. Young Charles cooked the meal over a fire of tiny dry sticks, and hardly a wisp of smoke rose to betray their camping place.

The moon came up and the night was warm. The fire died to embers. The men got ready to roll in their blankets and

46

sleep. But before they did so, one man drew another aside.

"Satisfied, Majors?"

"More than satisfied!" Mr. Majors said with emphasis. "I heard it said that he was the toughest and the keenest plainsman around here. The way he got us out of that scrape yesterday and avoided trouble today has me convinced. Yes, Charles is our man if we can get him."

At the end of the journey Mr. Majors talked to Charles.

"Do you know how letters travel from New York to San Francisco, Charles?" he asked.

"I've never had occasion to send a letter anywhere," answered Charles. "There's not much letter-writing in these parts."

"Well," said Mr. Majors, "there are plenty of letters going from one part of our country to the other. The trouble is the time that's needed. It takes weeks and months to get a letter from the East Coast to the West."

"You can cover considerable ground on horseback in a month," said Charles thoughtfully.

"The letters don't go by horseback. They travel by ship to Panama, then overland to the West Coast. Then up the coast by ship. I've an idea that it can be done faster than that, and I want you to help me, Charles."

Charles listened while Mr. Majors explained his plan. (In those days there was train service from New York to St. Joseph, Missouri, but no farther west.)

"From St. Joseph on, I want relays of the toughest, the keenest, and bravest young men I can find," Mr. Majors said. "They will have short stages and the finest horses we can get. They will need to ride in winter and summer, through sun and storm, night and day."

Charles's eyes brightened. The idea sounded interesting. There might be some fine adventures riding like that.

"Nothing must interfere with the mail," said Mr. Majors.

"It must go through so fast that in ten days a letter will be in San Francisco."

"Ten days' riding?"

"No. Ten days from New York to San Francisco, train and all."

"You must have worked out a plan," suggested Charles thoughtfully.

"We have. We are going to set up 198 stations from St. Joseph to San Francisco. We'll need five hundred of the best, speediest, and most enduring horses that we can find—and eighty riders." He paused and looked at Charles. "It will take more than pluck," he said. "Carrying the mail is an important business. It's a responsibility. The young men must be able to keep clear of trouble—no drinking, no fighting, no gambling or quarreling. And they must be honest and faithful."

Charles was looking more and more interested.

"It's a dangerous job, Charles. Interested?"

"Might be," said Charles briefly.

Mr. Majors brought out a rough map. "We're picking only the best men. I'd want you to help pick the men for this part of the country and have charge of them. And your own ride would be from here to here." He pointed out a section on the map.

"Not so long a ride!" said Charles.

"But it's a bad stretch in winter." Mr. Majors was watching Charles quietly. "Here's the point. Rain or storm, snow or sleet, blizzard or drought, war or peace, Indians or highwaymen, the mail must go through! The man before you is due at your station a certain time. You must be saddled and mounted at that time. When he arrives there must be no delay in transferring the mail pouch. It will be done before his horse stops. You will go on at all speed to the next station. Yours will be a night ride."

Young Charles smiled a slow smile. He could imagine that race through the night. Dangerous, yes, but exciting.

"There's one other thing," said Mr. Majors. "Our outfit is going to have the finest horses and the best horsemen. We must have men who are of fine character. We are choosing only men who are willing to sign this pledge." He laid on the table before the young man a statement, written in a clear, plain hand. "Read it," he said, "and read it carefully."

Charles read: "I do hereby swear before the great and living God that during my engagement and while I am an employee of Russell, Majors, and Waddell, I will under no circumstances use profane language; that I will drink no intoxicating liquors; that I will not quarrel or fight with other employees of the firm; and that in every respect I will conduct myself honestly, be faithful to my duties, and so direct all my acts as to win the confidence of my employers. So help me God."

It was a stiff pledge. Most of the horsemen of that wild western country did freely all those things that were forbidden in the pledge.

"The mail's a responsibility," Mr. Majors went on slowly. "We can't risk having weak men. And besides, we want our riders to act in a godly way."

Young Charles thought it over. "I'll make the pledge," he said. "It's not asking too much."

Mr. Majors' eyes shone with pleasure. He looked with satisfaction at the long, lean figure before him. He didn't need to be told that Charles would be equal to anything that might come up. "Wish I could be as sure of all of them as I am of this man," he thought to himself.

Young Charles signed the pledge. Mr. Majors pulled from his saddlebags a small leather-bound Bible. "We don't ask any pledge about reading the Bible, Charles," he said. "That's any man's own affair. But carry this little Book with you and read it. Reading the Book will make it easier to keep the pledge you have signed."

Over and over again Mr. Majors talked to one man and another. At last all had been selected. Each one had signed the pledge. Each one had his little leather-bound Bible and his trusty horses.

The day of April 3, 1860 arrived. A great crowd waited at the railway station at St. Joseph, Missouri. The train came puffing in—late! With all haste the mail, in which that first day were forty-nine letters, five telegrams and some newspapers, was stuffed into the leather saddlebag that was to carry them, and the gaily dressed, high-booted, eagle-eyed young rider swung into his saddle and was off.

Darkness came. Still the rider sped on. Four times he changed horses. And then at the end of a stretch of seventy-five miles another rider swung into the trail beside him. As they raced along together, the mail pouch was handed from the first man to the second. On and on and on! The thunder of hoofs was stilled only for the brief seconds when each rider swung from a tired horse to the one held waiting beside the trail. On and on and on!

So began the shuttle service of the Pony Express. Through sun and rain, through spring and winter, through calm and storm the men rode. Young Charles and the others never failed.

In the days between their wild rides carrying the mail, they lived according to their pledge, and many a one found comfort and help in the little leather-bound Book that went with him, in sunshine or storm, along the trail of the overland express.

9: White Sails and Blue Sea

New Zealand (1874)

ALL ashore that's going ashore!" bawled out the mate of the good ship *Surat*. The passengers on deck said their last good-bys to their friends. The ropes that tied the ship to the dock were tossed free.

Slowly the *Surat* started moving. The space between the vessel and the pier widened foot by foot. They were off!

Richard and Peggy stood beside their parents, watching everything with the deepest interest.

" 'Tis a year you will always remember, Richard and Peggy," said their father solemnly, "the year 1874, when you set sail from England for a new world and a new life."

Slowly the *Surat* moved out from the harbor. A fair wind was blowing and one after the other, the great sails were set. They filled with the following breeze. The prow cut through the waves faster and faster. The ship was on its way to New Zealand.

It was after they were out of sight of land that the captain called the passengers together. He had instructions to give them. He told them of the rules under which they must live on shipboard, and reminded them how the common safety and comfort of all depended upon the actions of each one. Then he said, "There is one thing more. A case was put on deck just before the ship sailed. In it there are three hundred New Testaments—a gift for the passengers of this ship. Each person will now be given one, as was requested by the donor."

Two tall sailors lugged a chest up to where the captain stood. It had already been opened. The captain passed out the New Testaments. Some of the passengers received them gladly. Others were indifferent. A few were scornful. But none refused a copy.

Their father wrote in Richard's and Peggy's copies, "On board the good ship *Surat*, upon sailing for New Zealand, in the year of our Lord, 1874."

Day followed day. Week followed week. Around the ship rolled the waters of the great Atlantic. On gray days the water and the sky were dull and uninteresting. On clear days the sparkling green and blue of the waves were a delight to behold.

The time came when the ship rounded the southernmost tip of South America. The passengers breathed a sigh of relief when they were beyond those bitter cold and dangerous straits.

Now they were in the vast Pacific. The ship plowed onward from sunset to sunrise and from dawn until dark. There were hot days and cold days, and once a spell of calm weather when the ship lay idle, its sails flapping in the quiet air. The passengers prayed for wind then, and the lookout, high up in the crow's nest, watched anxiously for signs of cloud or wind on the horizon. A sudden storm might swoop upon them, lashing the sea into great waves, and the ship would be in danger.

Weeks went by as the ship moved slowly across the Pacific. Months had passed since the passengers had left England. But they knew that at last they were nearing the end of their journey.

Richard and Peggy and the other children on board were busy with their lessons. Richard's mother and some of the other women had planned for school work to go on all during the trip. The youngsters had been glad enough for something to fill the long, eventless days. They had used their New Testaments for classbooks, and many were the verses and passages that they had learned by heart. All but the very youngest could read almost any part of the New Testament.

"No school tomorrow!" said Peggy. "It's New Year's Day, and Mamma has said that we may have a holiday."

The children went to bed that night in great anticipation. Tomorrow was New Year's Day and it was also the day on which the captain expected to sight land. They could hardly wait. Who would be first to catch sight of the welcoming shores?

But there were some on the ship who weren't waiting to celebrate New Year's Day tomorrow. The sailors had laid by the extra rations of liquor that each had been given daily, according to the customs of those olden times.

"New Year's Eve and time to get drunk," muttered one with a wink. "Let's to it, comrades!"

And get drunk they did—so drunk that the ship, under a stiffening breeze, plunged ahead with its crew lying useless in the forward hold.

The captain and the mate did their best to guide the vessel through the darkness without a lookout. The passengers, frightened, huddled together on the deck, with empty casks for life preservers fastened to the sleeping children.

Rocks were ahead! But the ship sped on!

Crash! The ship struck a reef, but lifted on the next wave and floated over it.

Crash! Again the ship floated free, but water was pouring now into a huge hole in her side.

Crash! This time the ship was fast on a rock, and each wave that followed battered against it.

How they got ashore the passengers never knew. But when morning came, they were all on land. They had lost everything they possessed. But their lives were safe and that mattered most to them. Some few had managed to tie treasured possessions to bits of board, which had been washed up by the waves and had lodged among the rocks of the New Zealand shore upon which they were cast.

That they had lost their family treasures and books and Bibles and the New Testaments that had been given them when the voyage started, troubled some of the passengers greatly. Such possessions were difficult to replace in this new land. Peggy and Richard remembered with sudden grief their treasured little New Testaments. The first books they had ever owned were lost in the sea.

Their mother comforted them. She put her hand into the deep pocket of her full skirt, such as all the women of those days wore. "When the ship came into danger last night," she said, "I slipped my New Testament into my pocket."

There it lay in her hands, water-soaked, as was all their clothing, but otherwise unharmed.

Richard's father slowly took the precious volume from her. "We can replace other things," he said, "but this is something that no other book could replace."

Richard and Peggy in their wet clothing shivered a bit. "It's a good thing we have one New Testament left," they said soberly. "We can all take turns using it."

Years and years later, when the old days were nearly forgotten, a man who had not even been born on that long-ago morning stood up before an audience. In his hands he held that little worn and water-stained book. He told the people before him the story of the voyage and of the wreck and read to them from the very copy that his grandmother had brought ashore with her on the New Year's morning of 1875.

"Everything else was lost," said Peggy's son. "But when my grandmother saved this little book, she saved the most important thing that the good ship *Surat* carried."

10: The Little Slave Girl of Madagascar

Madagascar (1882)

BIRDLING, the newly captured slave child, was quivering all over with sobs. She tried hard to control herself, for the slave master was looking angrily in her direction. Finally he came and stood over her, whip in hand.

"Have done with weeping," he commanded sternly. "Would you have me lash you?"

Birdling stopped crying and looked at him in utter horror. "Lash me?" she almost whispered. "You wouldn't!"

"And why not?" he answered roughly. "No longer are you the pampered pet of some foolish mother. You are nothing but a slave. In your home village who cared what happened to slaves?"

He strode away with a final warning. "The weeping is to stop. How shall I sell you tomorrow if your face is all swollen with tears?"

He had startled Birdling into stopping her tears. Fear of a whipping forced her to control her sobs.

What he had said was true. She knew it. All too true. No one in Madagascar cared what happened to slaves, not even in her own home village, now far, far away in the south. If the slaves bothered their owners, they were made to suffer for it. Certainly crying and sobbing would have received stern punishment.

Birdling made herself think of things other than home. She began to look around her. She pushed the sights and sounds of this new town between her and the memory of the laughter-filled happy home from which the slave raiders had snatched her. Her mother had been away making a visit in the next village and her father had been out hunting in the mountains when she and others of the village had been captured. So she had hope that her parents were safe. She dared not think of their grief when they came gaily home and found her gone. They would miss their Birdling, as they had always called her, but they would know that a pretty child such as she was would perhaps be sold into a good home.

Birdling's tears soon dried. Once she began to look around her she became interested in what was going on. She ate the sweet fruit that was brought her, although she did not know its name. She watched people go by, some in fine, rich clothes, attended by slaves. She wondered whether when morning came she would be following the litter in which some rich woman was carried by big, full-muscled slaves. She wondered whether she would be going through the noisy streets among the jostling crowds to a new home.

Morning came and Birdling, as she waked to strange surroundings, nearly wept again. But the bustle around her caught her attention and she was soon a part of it all. The newly captured slaves were being made ready for sale.

Birdling was given a simple garment, and her hair was arranged in childlike style. Not for nothing had the keeper of slaves spent her life in making little new slave girls attractive to would-be purchasers.

Then came a time of waiting. The rich did not arrive too early at the market. Others came and bought some of the lower-priced slaves. Once in a while someone would ask the price of Birdling, looking at her as she sat, half-fearful, half-expectant, in the shade of a huge, flowering tree, with the other slaves grouped near by.

But such ones always turned away on hearing the price that was being asked for her, although one or two said under the breath, "A beautiful child. They'll get what they're asking for her."

The sun still had not climbed high above the eastern horizon when a handsome litter arrived, carried by four slaves. A fifth carried a shade over the richly dressed young woman who rode in it. The slave master sprang to his feet. The lady in the litter must have some special need to have come herself and so early in the day. Of course it was wise to come early so that one might have the pick of the day's offerings. But often a trusted slave or an elderly relative was sent to make the choice.

"It is a house girl that I need," the young lady remarked, leaning over the side of the litter. The bearers still held it aloft, standing quietly while their mistress let her eyes rove over the group of dejected captives. Their sorrow did not trouble her. It hardly occurred to her that slaves might have hearts and be sad. Slaves were something she had been used to all her life, and she regarded the feelings of a slave as she would those of a favorite dog. She knew that some of the slaves she was looking at had very likely been torn from their homes and families, but that was the usual way of securing servants when the supply was low.

One captive was not looking sad. It was Birdling. She was so interested in the appearance of the rich young lady and her litter that she was examining her with eager curiosity. No such person as she had ever entered Birdling's simple home!

"That girl there!" The young lady pointed to Birdling. "She looks intelligent. And she is attractive. Let her stand forth."

Before Birdling knew what was happening, the sale had been made and she had become the property of the rich young lady. Soon the litter was being borne swiftly through the gathering morning crowd. Birdling was trotting along behind, breathing hard as she tried to keep up to the quick steps of the trained litter bearers. A huge slave strode along beside her to make sure that she made no attempt to escape.

He chuckled to himself at the hop, skip, and jump with which the new little slave moved.

Birdling was too young to have many duties, and she learned those she was given with a quickness that surprised and pleased her new mistress. It pleased her, too, that the child did not cry and fret.

"Were you born in slavery, Birdling?" she asked her carelessly one day.

For a moment Birdling's eyes were flooded with tears. Then she stood up as straight as she could, blinked back the tears and answered quietly, "No, Mistress. My home was in the south. It was from there that the raiders snatched me. My parents did not even know."

Her mistress' face clouded. "Ah! I had not guessed. And you so very young! You keep so cheerful, Birdling mine. I would never have guessed." Then she frowned. "Never before have I had any slaves that were born free. I do not like to think that one of my slaves was once free. Better never to have tasted freedom than to lose it. But at least you are as well off with me as a slave child may be?" She made the last statement into a question.

Birdling smiled. "Mistress, you have made me happy and contented," she answered truthfully.

Just the same there were times when Birdling was lonely —lonely with a loneliness that began at her toes and crept through her to her fingertips. She would slip away then, if no one was needing her help, down to the bottom of the garden slope. Under the big trees there she would sit down. Pulling a book from her garment, where she carried it, she would read.

The book was one that she had been reading at the moment that the slave raiders swooped down into the village. Without even thinking, she had clung to it when they carried her away and she had been allowed to keep it. It was her only book—the New Testament in the language of Madagascar.

No one in the household where she now lived was a Christian. But all the other slaves were amused at the sight of the pretty little slave girl sitting under the big trees at the foot of the garden slope. They used to creep down to look and to listen to her, reading, as the custom was, out loud. None of them could read. Not even their mistress could read. Only the educated slave who was overseer of the slaves and of the household could make sense out of the queer black and white marks in books.

All the household soon knew about Birdling's book, and that she could read it. But no one told the mistress.

"Who knows?" they said. "Our mistress is gentle and kind. But if it should offend her that a slave girl knows how to read, she might punish her, or forbid her to use her book, or even take it from her." So they kept the book a secret.

One hot summer afternoon Birdling's mistress wandered out into the garden in search of a breeze. She went down the slope where she had seldom been. As she walked she heard a low voice speaking but saw no one. Out of curiosity she followed the sound. There, at the foot of the slope, curled up on the gnarled root of a huge tree, she found Birdling, earnestly reading.

"What is this? Is it reciting a story you are, Birdling?"

Birdling stood up respectfully. She hid the small book behind her at first, then drew it forward. "No, Mistress, I was reading in my Holy Book."

"Reading? Can you read, Birdling?"

"Yes, Mistress. My father taught me."

Other slaves were standing uneasily in the background by then. Would the mistress be angry? Or would she be amused? To their astonishment she was neither.

"Do you think you could teach me to read, Birdling?"

"Oh, yes, Mistress. It is not hard." The slave girl's eyes lit up with happiness. "With joy I would teach you."

Lessons began, and the New Testament was the textbook. There was no other book from which to learn.

Birdling started with some of the stories that Jesus told. She helped her mistress to learn how to read one story after another.

"But this is interesting!" cried the mistress. "These stories are wonderful!"

Birdling had to explain what some of the stories were meant to teach. Then her mistress wanted to know who the storyteller was. "Who was this Jesus?" she asked.

So the next reading lesson was from the Gospel of *Luke*. The little slave girl helped her mistress to begin reading the story of the starry night when Jesus was born. They read of how the angels sang as the glory of heaven shone down on earth and the Baby cradled in a manger.

The reading lesson came to an end early that day. "It takes too long. Read me the rest of the story," demanded the mistress. So Birdling read, while Mistress and older slaves listened enthralled to a story they had never heard before.

The mistress loved the stories. No lesson went by without reading a story. But Birdling did not pass by the teachings, nor the words of Jesus about himself, nor the events of history that followed the day of Pentecost.

"Come over when the sun is low," the mistress would send a message to her friends. "I have a new slave—a mere child. She can read! From a book she reads. And the book has in it the strangest and most winning stories and teachings I have ever heard. Come over and hear my Birdling read."

Perhaps the mistress wanted her friends to discover that she herself had learned to read! For she always took the book from Birdling's hands and opened it to this place and to that place. She would read slowly and clearly, to the surprise and envy of her friends.

"Birdling," said her mistress one day, "put aside the book and talk to me instead. Tell me how to become a follower of Jesus."

It was nothing surprising to Birdling that her mistress should want to become a Christian. How could one help but want to follow Jesus? How could one help but worship God, who loved earth people so much that he sent Jesus to be their Lord and Saviour?

But oh, how surprised Birdling was when, one day later on, her mistress called all her slaves before her! "You all know," she said very slowly, "that I am become a follower of Jesus. And being so, I cannot hold any child of God my slave."

And with that she freed them all and had no longer any slaves.

What a day of joy that was! The slaves could hardly believe their ears. To be freed! To belong no longer to anyone, but each to own his own self! To ask no man or woman whether one might come or go, but like the breeze to wander wherever one's desire led one! The slaves were overcome with joy.

Some sped to homes almost forgotten. Others stayed with the mistress and worked for wages, loyally and faithfully, as before they had worked from necessity.

Birdling went back to her father's home. She entered the house almost as one risen from the dead and brought with her happiness more than could be measured. Then she returned to live with and care for the mistress she had come to love.

One long journey they took, the two of them, and a band of helpers traveled with them. They went to where there were missionaries. They begged that the church send missionaries to their town in Madagascar to teach and to lead the new

Christians in the Christian way. And in answer to that plea missionaries did come from a faraway land. But Madagascar and its climate were strange to them. Disease seized them, and one by one they died. So again, there was no one to lead and to teach the new followers of Jesus.

Yet the mistress was not discouraged. With the Bible in her hands she read and prayed and listened to the thoughts that God gave her. And with quiet persistence she taught everyone who was willing to learn from her.

Gradually there grew up in her town on the lovely island of Madagascar, so big an island that it is a country all of itself, a church with many, many members.

"And all because a lonely little slave girl read aloud from her New Testament," the Christians of that town will tell you proudly. "And because the heart of a rich young woman was open to the teachings of the Word of God to accept them and to live her life by them."

II: The Word of God Is My Sword

New Zealand

KATU, the Maori chief's son, lay awake on his mat. He could see through the open door the black outline of the mountains around the New Zealand valley where his tribe was living. High in the air they towered, cutting a pattern of craggy beauty against the black sky filled with blazing stars. Over against the tallest peak stood the Southern Cross, although Katu did not know that group of stars by its foreign name. He lay thinking of another night when he and his father's slave boy, Ripahua, had gone hunting and had watched the stars against the mountains while they spent the night beside their campfire.

"Ripahua has been gone for long months," thought Katu. "It is time for my uncle to come back from his journey to Paihia. It will be good to see Ripahua again." Ripahua had been loaned to Katu's uncle, to be his servant on the six-hundred-mile trip to the big town where he had gone on affairs of business.

A long day's march from the hut where Katu lay, Ripahua slept beside the trail. He was nearly home from his adventurous trip. What stories he would have to tell of Paihia, for a most unusual thing had happened to him in the months that he had been there! He had been to school! The business of Katu's uncle had required more time than he had thought. Someone had said to him, "Why not let the slave boy go to the mission school? It would be a great thing to take back to the chief a slave boy who can read and write!" Katu's uncle had agreed. Now, months later, Ripahua was nearly back to the tribe where he would be the only one who could put down words on paper and know what the meaning of the markings was. And he would be the only one who could take up a book and work out the thoughts that others had put down there.

Morning came. Katu rose from his mat and went about the day's work. Ripahua and the others of the traveling party were up early and on the trail. Ripahua's feet trod eagerly over the long miles that must be covered if they were to reach home by nightfall.

The rest of the group were as eager as he, and only very short stops were made to rest. So it was soon after sunset that they sent up the shout letting the settlement know that friends were entering.

After that, it was not many moments before a clamoring, chattering crowd were around them. Everyone had questions to ask about the journey and their health and how matters had gone with them.

At last Katu's uncle turned to the chief. "Here, O my brother, I return to you your slave, Ripahua. Good and useful has he been to me. But I return him to you more valuable than when I took him away, for during the months that I have been in Paihia he has been to school. He has come back to you with learning in his head!"

There was silence for a moment while everyone looked at Ripahua. To think that a slave boy had acquired learning! They gazed at him as if learning might have caused him to grow spots, or have changed his appearance in some other way. But Ripahua only smiled his old flashing smile and kept a becoming silence in the presence of his masters. He must not speak until spoken to. Then questions leaped at him.

"What have you learned?" demanded Katu, the chief's son. "Is writing among the learnings that you have gained?"

"Writing is among them," answered Ripahua, holding his head proudly.

"And reading?" asked Katu's cousin. "Can you make words with meaning from the little marks on paper?"

"That also I can do."

Many were the questions that were asked Ripahua. Even the chief had matters on which he wished replies. Ripahua breathed a sigh of relief when that frowning old warrior dismissed him, satisfied with what he had to say.

A few days later Katu and his cousin were talking earnestly to Ripahua about what he had learned. "Teach us also to read and write," they said.

"And why not? But—" and Ripahua scowled in deep thought—"we have not a single book, not even a page from a book! How can you learn to read with nothing from which to read?"

Katu and his cousin looked very unhappy. "You will have to make the writing. From it we will learn to read."

But Ripahua knew it would not be the same. "The words that are printed look different from the words that are written," he told them.

Suddenly Katu leaped to his feet. "I know! I know!"

He rushed away.

"Where has he gone?" wondered Ripahua. And the cousin of Katu shook a puzzled head.

In a moment Katu was back. He was waving in the air a little tattered book. "Here!" he shouted. "Here is a book. From it we shall learn to read. Now teach us, Ripahua!"

"Not so fast!" Ripahua reached out and took the book and examined it. "The Gospel according to Luke," he read slowly and with wonderment. "We had one like this at the mission school. Katu, from whence came this book?"

Katu had a strange story to tell.

His father, the chief, was a great warrior. He used to lead his tribe on raids. They would steal into the territory of neighboring tribes. With wild war cries they would descend upon their unwary neighbors and kill and plunder. Then they would go off, leaving the villages ablaze with fire. The name of Katu's father was feared and his raids dreaded for miles around. On one of the raids they had killed many persons.

"It was on the body of a little girl that this book was found," Katu finished his tale. "My father took it and brought it home, not knowing what it might be. He thought it might have some great power of magic about it."

Ripahua turned the book over and over in his hands. He had a moment of being sorry for the little girl, so needlessly killed in useless fighting. But so many people were left dead when tribal raids were over, that even Ripahua did not think much about it. The book in his hands was a different matter. It was printed in the Maori language.

"You can learn to read from it," he said with satisfaction. "You can take turns using it."

But Katu and his cousin had no notion of taking turns! "Not so! We will divide it," they said.

So the little Gospel of *Luke* was torn into two sections. Ripahua, the slave boy, became Ripahua the teacher. And the chief's son and his cousin began to learn to read and to write.

Weeks went by. Katu and his cousin could read a little from their pages. At first they read only sounds and words. Then they read whole sentences. How delighted was Katu the first time he read something that he could really understand!

The boys began to talk about the matters of which the book spoke. They began to think of Jesus as he walked and talked and helped and healed those to whom he came in Galilee and Judea.

"What does this teaching mean, Ripahua?" Katu would ask.

All too often Ripahua was as puzzled as the other two. "Truly I do not know. Its words are too strange to me," he would say. All three would read and think and argue. Too often they could not find clear understanding for all that worried them.

Yet understanding about one thing was clear. They all three came to love the Lord Jesus and to wish to be his followers. "Ah! If I had but lived in those days when he was on earth!" Katu would say. "Think, Ripahua, think! We could have followed him from one place to another. We might have seen him and heard his voice. We could have asked him what he meant when his words were not quite clear to our dull understanding."

"Back in Paihia," said Ripahua, "there are missionaries. They have understanding. Sometimes they send teachers to make all things clear to those who ask for them."

"We will go and ask for a teacher," decided Katu.

The chief's consent to the trip was quickly sought and granted. Back over the trail that Ripahua had traveled went Katu and his cousin. For the long six hundred miles they traveled.

"We have come for a teacher," they said to the missionary when they had arrived at Paihia. They told about Ripahua who had come home with learning but no book, and about the little Gospel of *Luke*, and of how they had used it as a reader and had come to love it for its words of wisdom. "Send us a teacher," they begged.

"Go back home," said the interested missionary. "It will be some time before I can come to you. But most surely I shall visit you, or I shall send someone to you."

Before the boys left, he talked to them for hours, making clear some of the things that they had longed to know about and putting their thinking into a straight path.

Katu and his cousin reached home. They told Ripahua

of all they had seen and heard and done. "Now," suggested Katu, "let us build a little chapel like the one they have at Paihia. Then when the missionary comes, he will have a place suitable for teaching."

The chief was willing. He gave the order, and soon a very simple little chapel rose. In it Katu and his cousin and Ripahua would gather the children, and sometimes the older people, and read to them the message of God's love, explaining it as best they could.

And one day, redeeming his promise, the missionary with his helpers arrived at the settlement of Katu's tribe. He was made welcome by the chief and was lodged with all honor. He talked much with the three boys. When he saw clearly how their hearts were set on becoming followers of the Lord Jesus, he baptized them in the little chapel that they had built. So, bidding them be steadfast, and leaving with them copies of the whole New Testament in Maori and guidance for their study, the missionary and his helpers went back to their own place.

Then Katu and his cousin and their friends began to think that what they had come to love so much was needed by others. They bought more copies of the New Testament. Taking as many as they could carry, they would go out and visit the people of their tribe in other settlements, reading to them and selling them the Book whenever any wished to buy.

After a time Katu began to visit the neighboring tribes. He went to the lands that his father had laid waste with fire and sword and spear. The people greeted him sullenly.

"Are you not afraid to come here?" they asked him at first. "Look yonder, where once a rich village stood. Even its ashes are melted into the earth. It was your father who did it."

But Katu only smiled. "That evil is done and over," he said. "Look at me. Do I carry a spear? Are there warriors behind me? Is there any sword in my hand to conquer and distress?"

Then the people became more friendly. "Truly, you have no sword. But why do you travel thus unprotected?"

Katu took from his bundle his copy of the New Testament. He held it up where all could see it. "Look!" he cried. "I have here the Word of God. I have come to teach it to you. It is my only sword. It will conquer hate and distrust. It will bring joy and peace into your lives!"

Then he sat down with the oldtime enemies of his father, and as friends they talked over the wonders of God's love. As brothers they looked into one another's eyes. And peace spread its wings over the land.

12: The Bible in Their Hearts
Poland

THE sun was setting as Karl Olsen trudged through the mud of the scarcely passable road to Barren Village.

"These roads of East Poland!" he muttered crossly. "Almost impossible they are! If I were not carrying the Bible to people who do not have it, I would not wear myself out on them."

Karl was used to wearing himself out in such travel. On the muddy country roads, far back from towns and pavements, he often sank halfway to his knees in the bog holes. Usually he was cheerful enough about it, but sometimes after a long day of bad going he felt tired, and his good nature wore thin.

When he began to think that he could go no farther, and lamplighting time sent gleams of light from the tiny windows of villagers' homes, Karl came within sight of Barren Village. As he drew closer, dogs growled fiercely at him. But Karl had a way with dogs. Otherwise he would have been attacked and injured many a time.

He knocked at the door of the first house.

A man opened it and stood on the threshold, looking out. From under his arms three children peeked at the stranger who had appeared out of the gathering dusk.

"A welcome," said the man seriously. "Enter."

But Karl did not come in. Not yet. "I am in search of a night's lodging, kind sir. I have money to pay for it and also for a meal. And I have a book from which to read stories. It has in it the most wonderful story the world has ever known."

Karl stood quietly waiting for the man to decide whether or not to take him in. Karl never pushed himself into people's homes. But usually one good look at his face won him a welcome.

"What say you, Marja?" The man addressed his wife. She came forward and examined Karl's face keenly.

"The night will be bitter cold," she said. "We have room and there is food enough." She turned back to her stove.

"Come in, then. Come in and warm yourself. I bear the name of Antoni Kowalski. And yours?"

"Karl Olsen," said the other. "I carry books to sell. I also read and tell stories to those in whose homes I lodge."

The children clustered around Karl as he seated himself by the big tiled stove that stood high at the side of the room.

Little Marja, named for her mother, and the oldest of the three children, smiled shyly at Karl. "A story?" she begged. Her father laughed.

"Never has little Marja had enough stories," he said. "But let our guest get his hands warm, child, before you pester him."

Karl was soon warm and comfortable. He opened his pack and took out a Bible.

"Here it is, the most precious Book in the world. Shall I read you a story from it? Here is a story told by Jesus to the people who gathered around him."

Karl opened the Bible. He read the story of the Good Samaritan. "You have been good Samaritans to me," he said. "You have taken me in and sheltered me. From the dark roadway and the danger of animals that would do me harm you have saved me."

Then it was time for supper. Karl enjoyed the hot food. The meal was simple peasant fare, but it was well prepared and strengthening.

Afterwards Marja and Antoni and little Marja and Jan and Zosia sat and listened while Karl told them story after story.

He told them about Joseph and David. He told of Solomon's building the beautiful temple, and of Daniel's being thrown into the den of lions. Before telling each story he opened the Bible to the right chapter. As he talked he would read a verse here and there, to put that part of the story into the exact words of the Bible.

Little Marja sighed with pleasure as Karl finally closed the Book. "Let us buy a Bible so that Father can read from it every evening," she begged. "Father is the only one in the village who can read," she explained proudly to Karl.

"We are too poor for books." Her father frowned.

"Those without this Book are poor," said Karl softly. "But those who have it, possess that which is better than riches."

"Please! Please!" begged little Marja. Finally her father yielded and bought the Bible. He set it in a place of honor in the house.

Karl stayed with the family for two days. He made friends with others in the village, but no one else would buy a Bible, or a New Testament, or even a Gospel. Karl was disappointed. It had meant so much to him to find, on the very night he arrived, a family ready to buy the whole Bible. He had hoped there would be others in Barren Village who would buy.

On the third day Karl left to go on to other towns and villages. As he plodded through the thick mud of the road, he kept thinking about how little he had sold.

"Ah well," said he to himself, "it is true that I go away from this place, but the Word of God remains behind. There is now a Bible in Barren Village where there was none before. And who knows what may happen?"

Winter came to East Poland, and long, long evenings when the sun set early and wolves roamed the countryside. No one stirred much from home, and there was little to do within. On such evenings Antoni would take down the Bible and read the stories that Karl had marked. He would read the teachings of Jesus from the chapters and verses that Karl had listed for him.

As he read aloud, Marja and little Marja and Jan and Zosia sat around and listened. Afterwards they would talk about what they had heard and wonder at it.

Sometimes a neighbor would come in. Antoni would reach for the Bible and say, "Listen to a thing I have found in this Book. Listen well and tell me what you think of such teaching."

He would read while the neighbor sat with head on one side, listening carefully. Then would come argument and conversation about the meaning of the teaching. The talk would be about what they themselves should do. The children would drink in the thoughts that were being discussed.

"Why should I forgive my enemy?" the neighbor would inquire. "Does the Book mean that I should chop wood for someone who stole part of my wheat crop? Surely it cannot mean that!"

"Who knows? It would be a strange way to act." And Antoni would shake his head doubtfully. "A strange teaching."

"Or this now—" and he would turn to another verse— "Do unto others as you would have them do unto you."

Little Marja and Jan listened as their father and one neighbor or another talked. They heard the teaching about doing as one would be done by discussed over and over again. They would look at each other and remember that when they were playing with other children they had not always acted in that kindly way.

How the change came about no one could tell, because it was all so slow that no one noticed what was happening until things were different. "Like yeast, working silently in dough," Jesus had said, when he talked about God's spirit at work in the hearts of men. And so it was in Barren Village. The teachings of God's Word began to change Antoni and his family and his neighbors and their friends and the way they thought and talked and acted. Barren Village began to blossom with kind thoughts and good deeds.

There came the day when Antoni and Marja and little Marja and Jan became followers of Jesus, not only in their hearts, but openly, before others. Zosia was too young to become a church member, but she, too, loved Jesus and tried to act as a child of God should.

Then others of the villagers found that they, too, wanted to be of the company of those who are called Christians.

One day Antoni and Marja made a count of those in Barren Village who were now followers of Christ. "One hundred ninety-eight, one hundred ninety-nine, two hundred," they counted. "If only Karl could know how much has come to this village from the one Bible he left here!"

It was the fact that they had just one Bible that began to worry the two hundred Christians of Barren Village. "Why did we not buy the Book when Karl was here?" they mourned. "Why did we let him carry away those precious copies?" But it was too late now to regret what had happened.

"Suppose Antoni's house should burn down," they worried. "What if a thief came in when all of us were working in the fields and stole our only Bible?"

"I know some of it by heart," said little Marja. "I know the story of Jesus and the children, and the Hundredth Psalm."

"I know the story of the Good Samaritan," said Jan. "I can say it without a mistake."

"My heart is full of many small verses that I have loved," offered Marja, "but I do not know any chapter from one end to the next."

That gave everyone an idea. "We must learn the whole

Bible," decided the two hundred Christians. "We must learn it by heart. Every part of it that we can possibly learn we will memorize."

So they made a plan. They first listed the verses and the chapters and the stories and the passages that they most loved and that had the teachings they thought were most important.

Then each person was given something to learn. The little children learned verses. The older children learned stories and short passages and psalms that were not too long. The grownups took the hard parts of the Bible to learn. They worked and worked on the memorizing.

Sometimes the Christians would get together and someone would start with the opening of the first chapter of a book, such as the Gospel of *Luke*. He would recite as far as his part went. Then the person who had the next part would stand and repeat his. Antoni would hold the Bible in his hand and follow the recitation to be sure it was correct, word for word. On and on would go the reciting. Each one knew where his part fitted into the whole.

The long winter evenings were busy now with reading and repeating and memorizing. It was surprising how much of the Bible was learned that first winter. And during the next two years still more was memorized.

The sun was setting one day as Karl Olsen trudged through the mud of the scarcely passable road to Barren Village. "Years ago," he was thinking, "I visited this place so far from everywhere. I sold but one copy of the Bible there. I sold it to the man in whose house I stayed. Now what was his name?" And Karl tried to dig out of his memory the name of Antoni. At last it came, for Karl had a good memory for names. He was glad. It was always pleasant to greet people by name. It was a pleasure to him and to the one whose name he had remembered.

As lamplighting time sent little gleams of light from the tiny windows of the village houses, Karl came once more to the door of Antoni and Marja. He knocked, wondering if they still lived there and if the three children were all still alive and well.

Little Marja came to the door this time. She was taller than her mother now and had grown older. After a moment's looking at the stranger who stood before her, Marja remembered him. She called out in delight, "Karl! Mama! Mama! It is Karl, come back after all these years!"

The family crowded around him then—Antoni and big Marja and Jan and Zosia. Word went flying around the village that Karl had come, and in a flash others were there, smiling and welcoming him.

Karl was confused beyond measure. Why such a greeting? How did they happen to remember him?

Little by little the story came out. Antoni produced the Bible, so worn that it was nearly ready to fall apart. Marja, interrupted a hundred times by others eager to join in the telling, told him how they had studied the teachings and how two hundred and more of the people of Barren Village had become followers of Jesus. But no one thought to tell Karl about learning the Bible by heart. That was something they had done for their own sakes and it did not occur to them that what they had done would be of interest to anyone else.

Next day they gathered for worship and Karl was with them. During the service he asked, hoping to get at least a few responses, "Shall we then, repeat from memory some of the verses we have come to love? Is there someone here who has learned a verse and would like to recite it?"

There was a moment's silence. Then Antoni asked, "Verses, or chapters?"

Karl looked as amazed and delighted as he felt. "Chapters!"

He asked, "Is there anyone here who knows a whole chapter of the Bible by heart?"

They told him then of how they had been seized with fear of losing their only Bible, and of how they had memorized it, chapter after long chapter, each taking a share. "Almost the whole Bible is learned and we are working now on the parts that are yet to be committed to memory," they told him with pride.

Jan recited and little Marja, and Zosia and all the other children, verse after verse and chapter after chapter. The minutes sped by. The older people recited some of the chapters they liked best.

Karl stayed in Barren Village for a week. The Christians, so far from all other Christians, had many questions to ask him. They bought all the copies of the Bible and of the New Testament and of the Gospels that he had with him.

"We have the Bible in our hearts," they said, "but no one of us has more than a small portion of the whole of it. And each of us needs it all."

"God's Word worked in the hearts and minds of the people here," thought Karl to himself as he lay in bed the night before he was to leave. "Only one copy of the Bible and see what has come of it!"

13: The Black Magic of Don Cornelio

Central America

So FAR as strangers could tell, the people of that Central American countryside were Christians. But when nights were dark and there was trouble such as sickness in the homes, the people forgot the Christian God. They remembered the black and bygone days when their ancestors worshiped the terrible, angry gods of darkness. Fear entered their hearts. They said, "Maybe our forefathers were right. Maybe the terrible gods are angry at us. Maybe that is why there is sickness."

Then they would think of Don Cornelio and his wife Doña Inez. They would send a message to them through the moonless night.

"Sickness is among us. The old gods must be angry. Come and help."

Don Cornelio and his wife would go to the village that was in trouble. They would work their dark spells and return to their home the richer for their labors.

In the village the sickness would sometimes grow less and stop. Then the people, not knowing the true cause of disease, would give credit to Don Cornelio's witchcraft. But sometimes the infection was strong. Suffering and death would continue. Then faith in Don Cornelio's black magic would grow less and the people would turn once more to the teaching of the priests.

One dark night Don Cornelio heard a knock at his door, long after most people were in bed. He smiled an unholy smile as he got up and went through the patio. He put his ear to a crack in the door and listened carefully to the sounds outside.

"Don Cornelio! Don Cornelio!" He could barely hear the whispered call.

"Who is there?"

"It is Miguel, Señor. Miguel, with a message from the Village of the Serpent."

Don Cornelio knew that it was someone wanting him to do black magic. Hundreds of years before, the towns and villages of the countryside had been given saint-names by the Spanish priests who came after Cortez. The priests had baptized the people and told them that they were Christians. The names that were tied to the old religion had been forbidden. But they had not been forgotten. So now when a man came in the dead of night and whispered, "The Village of the Serpent," using the old forbidden name instead of a saint-name, Don Cornelio knew that thoughts of the old gods were flying through the night.

He unbarred the heavy wooden door. He let the messenger in.

"Señor, come," the anxious traveler begged through the darkness. "Illness runs like wildfire through our village. We have made offerings in the church. But the priest only demands larger gifts and still the sickness breaks out afresh. Could it be that the old gods, the terrible ones, are angry? Do they know that no offerings are being made on their old altars? That they are forgotten in the villages?"

"Why should they not be angry? How long is it since the foolish ones of your village have torn the heart from a black cock and laid it dripping upon the hidden altar?" Don Cornelio asked coldly.

"Too long! Too long!" the messenger admitted.

After seeming to hesitate, Don Cornelio spoke. "Tomorrow," he said, "tomorrow we will come to the Village of the Serpent. Let all be ready!"

The man went out again into the night, to find his way

back by the light of the late-rising moon to the waiting people at home.

The next day Don Cornelio and his wife got out the tools of their black magic. They slipped away from their house and went over the mountain trails to the Village of the Serpent. They lodged at the inn, as did any ordinary travelers, except that they paid nothing for food and room.

The priest knew that there was something stirring in the village. He eyed Don Cornelio sternly. "Will you come to Mass, my son?" he invited.

Don Cornelio and his wife made excuses. Those who deal in black magic and who worship the terrible ones do not go to Mass and ask the blessing of God upon themselves. They are afraid of the anger of God because they know they are doing evil. So they remain far from churches and they have nothing to do with priests.

Late, late that night, Don Cornelio and his wife joined the anxious villagers at the edge of the village. Only a few knew of the trail. Only a few had followed it to its end. A secret pathway led to a cave hidden behind fallen rocks on the hillside.

The little company crept behind the rocks and entered the cave. In a cleft at the back was a passageway to another cave. No one would have dreamed that a second cave lay there. The knowledge of it had been passed down from father to son through hundreds of years.

The village leader passed through the narrow opening. Don Cornelio followed, squeezing through and muttering curses softly to himself. After him came Doña Inez and the others. A dim lantern lighted the way of those in front, but those following had to feel their way along in the darkness that closed in all too quickly about them.

There was not much to be seen in the inner cave. The lantern light shone down on a block of stone, with a scooped-out place in the center and a runway for the blood of the old-time sacrifices. The walls faded out in utter blackness. Somewhere in the dark the dry rustling of a snake could be heard.

Doña Inez shivered. For all that she helped Don Cornelio with his witchcraft, she was often afraid—afraid of the terrible ones and afraid of the living snakes and other dangers of the night expeditions.

The light of the lantern was put out. There in the pitch-black darkness Don Cornelio began to chant the words of his magic spells. The chants rang wild in the echoing cave, as he worshiped the terrible ones. With the old, old magic he made sacrifice to the old gods.

Fear and dread filled the cave. For the terrible ones had no love in their hearts, the frightened people knew. They were not like God, of whom they had heard in church. Ah, if they might only believe that what the priest said was true—that the terrible ones did not exist—that there was only God!

At last the worship was over. The lantern was lit once more. The little group stumbled away from the place of terror.

The next day Don Cornelio and his wife went home. They were satisfied with their night's work and well paid in coin and goods.

After such trips Don Cornelio would take his books of black magic and study them anew, seeking fresh spells to learn. Most of all he searched for the spell that would really bind the terrible ones to his will. He hoped to find the secret words that would give him power over the old ones, so that his magic would always work.

During the winter months, when travel was hard because of the bogged-down roads and there was not much to do in the villages, Don Cornelio had leisure. He and his wife often went to visit in the towns. On one such visit they wandered into the reading room of the Central American Mission. They were welcomed by the workers in that place, open for anyone to come into and read. They found a Bible in their own language.

Don Cornelio was surprised. The priests had no Bible for the people to read. He had always liked books and he was interested in this one. That day he read the Book of the Christian religion that he found in the reading room of the Evangelical mission station.

As he went from big town to big town, he and his wife found other mission reading rooms. They took to going into them and reading from the Bible and talking over its teachings with the workers at the mission. They came to look forward to those visits.

Don Cornelio began to be worried. The Bible told of God as One who is great, wise, loving, and powerful. The image of the terrible ones began to dim in his mind. They seemed to shrink in importance. They did not seem so real.

Doña Inez was puzzled. She noticed that her husband spoke less and less of his search for the greatest of all spells. She watched closely but she seldom saw him opening his books of black magic.

"Wife-of-Mine," he said one day, "my spirit is very troubled."

"Tell me, then," she urged.

"The priests are right. The terrible ones do not exist. There is only God."

Doña Inez drew a long breath as if she had suddenly been freed from walking in fear. "Are you sure?"

"Sure as a man may be! There cannot be both God and the terrible ones. My mind clings to the thought of God. As a flower opening to the sun, my heart opens to him. When I think of him, gladness like the blue sky fills my mind, and the dark, terrible thoughts die out."

His wife's face was flooded with relief. "I have always been afraid of the old ones. But I was more afraid not to believe in them. It is joy to know that they do not exist."

Don Cornelio still looked worried. "But our living! It is tied up in one bundle with the terrible ones. If we no longer do black magic, where will our beans and our tortillas come from? How will we eat? How will come the money for our clothing? Where shall I pick up the coins to pay rent to our landlord?"

Doña Inez looked troubled. "That is a difficulty, indeed," she admitted.

So for a time Don Cornelio practised his witchcraft, although with more and more unhappiness. He still crept through the moonless nights to make sacrifices and to chant spells before the hidden altars. Yet each time he was more disturbed in mind than before. Each time his feet carried him with lagging steps to the villages where the troubled people looked on him with such faith and such hope.

One day he and Doña Inez stopped at the mission. They were sick at heart, for no one who lives a lie can be happy, and they were doing that which they themselves felt to be evil.

Don Cornelio leafed through the Bible restlessly. He could not bear to read about God. God was goodness, and he was giving his life to evil. Must he stop reading the Bible?

His eyes kept catching at phrases as he turned the pages. He came to the Epistle of *I Peter*, to the end of the first chapter. The words stopped him. He read them carefully. " 'All flesh is as grass, and all the glory thereof as the flower of grass. The grass withereth, and the flower falleth: But the word of the Lord abideth for ever. And this is the word of good tidings which was preached unto you.' "

"True! Ah, how true!" murmured Don Cornelio. "Nothing else endures. Nothing else matters. Nothing!"

He turned to Doña Inez as they sat alone in the quiet reading room. "Nothing matters but God," he said to her earnestly. "Nothing at all. I see it now, Wife-of-Mine. We cannot go on believing in God in our hearts and yet earning our living by making spells and sacrifices to the old ones that do not exist. Let us burn up our black magic books, Inez. I can find some other work to do so that we shall not go hungry."

Doña Inez looked at him with sober, considering eyes. It would be hard to do without the gifts, the money, and the easy living. But it would be worth while.

"I am willing," she said, "more than willing."

So it came about that one evening when the rain poured down and mud was thick in the streets, the little chapel of the mission was filled to overflowing. Word had gone out that Don Cornelio, whom everyone suspected of practising black magic, and his wife, Doña Inez, had something they wished to say to the Evangelical Christians. Through the rain the people came to hear what that something could possibly be.

It was not easy for Don Cornelio to stand up before the church people. Many of them were strangers to him. Nor was it easy to admit openly about the black magic and the secret spells. It was harder yet to tell about the sacrifices and the worship of the terrible ones at the hidden altars in the caves. The church people shrank back in dismay as Don Cornelio spoke.

But Don Cornelio went on bravely. He told about reading the Bible. He told how the love of God had come flooding into his soul like dawn over the mountains after a stormy night. He told how he had resisted giving his heart to God, how he had feared for his bread and his clothing and his comfortable home. The feelings of the church people warmed to him in their sympathy.

At last Don Cornelio and Doña Inez brought forward their books of black magic—old volumes handed down through long generations. They brought the charms they had made and the written spells.

"We are ready to burn them," they said. "We will wipe clean from our minds the spells and the charms we know, as the winds blow clouds from the sky when the rainy season is over."

The rain outside had stopped. In the patio beside the chapel a fire was built. One by one the books and the charms were placed upon it. The flames roared high through the dark night, and at last there was nothing left but a handful of ashes.

Don Cornelio held his hands, palms up, to the sky. "The books of black magic are gone," he said, " 'but the word of the Lord abideth for ever!' It abideth for ever and by it will we build our lives."

"Amen," said the people reverently. "And may God guide us all to do the same."

14: The Strength to Be Good

Korea

K IM shivered a little as he lay curled up on the mat that was his bed. His mother frowned anxiously in the dim light. They both listened hard. It was late, late in the night.

Yes, the sound was getting nearer. Pak was coming home and he was roaring drunk.

Tears crept down the cheeks of Kim's mother. Pak had worked so hard the past week. He had taken the week's garden stuff to market, firmly resolved to sell quickly and to bring home his hard-earned money for the family to use.

"It has happened again," mourned Kim. "He has gotten drunk, and the money is now in the hands of the gamblers."

Pak was very drunk indeed when he came into the little Korean farmhouse. His clothing, which had been fresh and neat as a careful housewife could make it when he left for town that morning, was torn and dirty. One eye was battered shut. His pockets, his wife knew, were empty.

When morning came and Pak woke, he was overcome with despair. He sat with his head bowed in his hands.

Then Kim and his mother did their best to comfort him. "You were tempted," Kim's mother said. "Never mind! We can live on vegetables again this week. Your coat can be mended. Kim can still wear his old sandals. They are not quite worn out. Next week, when you go to the market, you will come back without getting into the hands of the gamblers or into a fight."

But Pak was discouraged clear to the bottom of his heart. "*Ai-yoh!*" he mourned aloud. "Was it for this we left our home? Was it for this we came to this monastery, far from the city? Is it then to be the same old story? Am I to work

from dawn to dusk in the monastery garden, and then fall
into temptation the moment my feet tread the city streets
again?" Pak nearly wept. For when he was himself, his
desire to do what was right was strong and keen. But he
had no strength to withstand the temptation to drink, to
gamble, and to fight.

"We might give a greater offering in the temple," his
wife suggested timidly.

Pak looked at her with sorrowful eyes. "This Buddhism!"
he protested. "It is a religion that says, 'Be good! Be good!'
But it gives me no strength with which to be so. Of what use
is it to put an offering on the altar? Does it make me less
quick to pour out my coppers for a drink? Does it keep me
from laying my silver on the gamblers' tables? Does it cause
my feet to turn aside from the brawling instead of walking
right straight into the midst of a fight? No!" Pak spoke
firmly. "No more offerings!"

Kim went with Pak to market the next week. He hoped
that he could help to keep his father away from temptation.

But once in the city, Kim was dismayed. No sooner had
part of the produce been sold than Pak was off, joyfully
leaving his son in charge of what was left. Kim sighed. He
had no heart to try to sell. What was the use? His father
would come back drunk and demand the rest of the money
to go gambling.

But as Kim watched his father's tall figure go toward the
place-of-drinking, he saw him stop and stand, listening to
something. Kim wished that he could find out what it was.

Minutes went by. Still Pak stood motionless. What in the
world was it that could keep him from going after a drink?
Kim sold what was left in the baskets as quickly as he could
and hurried to his father's side.

A man, neatly dressed and with a smiling face, was reading
from a little book. Just as Kim came up he closed the little

book and began to talk. "Buy one!" he urged. "In this little book you will find glad tidings of salvation. Its teaching will save you from wickedness."

Pak was talking under his breath. "Save me from wickedness? No! Ah no! Nothing can do that!" He noticed Kim standing beside him. "Did I not tell you to stay by the baskets?"

"I have sold all, my father."

"The money?" Pak eagerly held out his hand.

"Let me keep it, my father. Only till we get home. Let me give it to my mother."

Dull red crept into Pak's face. "Even my son knows I am not to be trusted with the money I earn," he said sadly. "Keep it, then, Kim, this once. But stay out of my sight, lest I snatch it from you and gamble it away."

The man who had been reading was listening. "Why gamble it away?" he asked politely. "A man such as you, by your looks, does not care for gambling." His gaze wandered to Pak's work-hardened hands.

"A worker, and a good worker, to judge by your hands," he said.

"True!" Pak was glad enough to talk. Anything to keep himself away from the place-of-drinking! "A good farmer. Things grow beneath my fingers. But there my good fortune ends."

The man with the book was interested. "How can that be?"

Pak liked the man. He liked his quiet courtesy. Perhaps this man, who had said his book could save him, would be able to help. "See you, sir, I work hard. I bring my produce here to market. And then, and then—"

He thrust out his hands in despair. "The gods alone know what devil comes to possess me. With the money in my hand I go to the place-of-drinking. And what is left I spend with the gamblers. And should there be a thread of an excuse for fighting, I fight."

Kim broke in. "But sir, he is a most good father. And if you could but see him work! No rest does he take but works from dawn to dusk to grow the food we need, my mother and I. Only it is as he says. He cannot bring home the money he has earned by his hard work."

The man looked thoughtfully at the farmer. Pak seemed like a person with plenty of determination. If only he could learn not to give way to his longing for strong drink and his love of gambling and fighting!

"There is no hope for me," whispered Pak.

"Ah, but there is!" The man brought out four little copies of the four Gospels. "Here you will find it, the way of salvation from your wrongdoing. Here you will learn of One who can give you strength to be good. Will you buy these small books, my friend? Will you spend money for these instead of going to the place-of-drinking?"

Kim made a motion to draw out the money as his father hesitated. But the keen eyes of the man saw him. He put out a hand in protest. "Your father it is who must choose. The way of salvation or the way of destruction. After one drink it would be too late to make the choice. He would be chained to his drinking and his gambling once more."

Pak still hesitated. How he longed to go and pour the strong but soothing drink down his throat! To feel no longer troubled, but boastful and ready to fight! But he was not altogether a weakling. The man who had left his home in town and gone to a lonely monastery garden far, far from friends and old haunts just so that he might be farther from temptation was able to make himself choose now.

He drew out the money. "I will buy."

"Good!" The man smiled as he handed over the four Gospels. "You will not regret your purchase. And now—"

Pak did not wait for him to finish. "Now I take the road home. For this once I return with my money unspent."

Yet he did not go right at once. He stopped at a stall, and with Kim's admiring help he bought for Kim's mother a new garment. Kim's eyes were bright with delight—delight that they were going home with the week's earnings in their pockets, delight at what his mother would say when she saw the new robe.

How short it seemed, that long road home! Pak was a new man. His unhappiness was gone. He had been to town. He had sold his produce in the market place. And by the help of a man with a book he was on his way home, with money in his pocket and his head up in the air.

Many were the merry tales he told Kim as they trudged along the road. Kim's love for his father was tinged with pride now—pride because he had left untouched that which tempted him.

It was nearing dusk as they reached the monastery. The smell of the incense the priests were offering drifted out over the walls.

"Buddhism," said Pak thoughtfully. "I do not know, Son-of-Mine, but my mind is beginning to tell me that the teaching of these books may be more to my liking than the old religion, which has not given me strength to do that which I know is right to do. We will see if the teaching in these new books can help."

Kim's mother straightened up from her work at the sound of voices. She glanced at the sky. Not even a star was showing and the color of sunset was beginning to make a glory of the sky. It could not be that Pak and Kim were arriving home! It could not be that!

And yet it was! Kim dancing with excitement, in spite of his feet being weary with the miles of walking. Pak with the light in his eyes that had been there when they both were young. So clear-eyed and merry! Nor was her amazement less when the new robe was brought forth, and the money that was left over was laid before her unbelieving eyes.

Then Pak began to explain. He told about the man and about the words read from the book that had caught his attention. He told about the man's saying that the teaching in the book would save him from wrongdoing, and about how he had chosen to buy the four little books and come right home.

They ate then, a hastily prepared meal. Afterwards, for so long as the light lasted, Pak read aloud to his wondering wife and to Kim the wonderful story that the Gospel writers had to tell.

Evening after evening, when toil in the garden was over, Pak read. His wife, moving silently about her work, listened. So also did Kim, and the three of them talked about what they had read and wished they could know more of the teaching.

Once more Pak went to market. With him went Kim. The man with the book was there, and Pak begged him to come to the monastery and visit him. That day for the second time, Pak and Kim went home early, heads in the air and money in their pockets. On this day Kim walked in new sandals, and his father carried a new short hoe for his garden work.

Again there was the happiness of return to a hoping wife and mother, and a new telling of all that the man with the book had said.

Weeks later the man came to visit. Still later a missionary followed in his tracks. Pak and his wife and Kim were by then following the road that the book showed them. They had become followers of Jesus.

"Strength to do right!" said Pak contentedly. "I have

found it, and no longer do I work in despair, knowing that it is all in vain, once temptation faces me."

He could laugh now, could Pak, when his old friends the gamblers tried to persuade him to risk his money upon a chance. He could shake his head easily and walk away from the place-of-drinking. He had no wish to become a boaster or to pick a fight. Kim went often with him to market. Life was still full of hard work. But mixed with the work there was joy, and for what more than that can a person ask of life?

There came a day when Pak, with his own goods sold out early, began to help the man sell books. The man watched him with deep attention. He found that Pak could sell ten Gospels and Bibles to his one.

"There stands a man who should be giving his life to taking the message of salvation to others," thought the man. "He should be one of us. For it is not everyone who can talk to people and help them to find the path to doing right."

So it came about that Pak too, after a while, became a man-with-a-book. Far and wide he went, trudging along the roads of Korea, through rain and sun. Far and wide he told the story of salvation. Far and wide he sold the Bible or the New Testament or the Gospels.

"Here is the Book," he would say, "that gives one strength to do what one knows is the right. I know, for through the teachings of this Book, I, who had no strength, gained it. And Pak the drinker, Pak the gambler and the brawler is he who now stands before you. Will you too, buy?"

15: The Search Among Thieves

Paraguay

SEÑOR Anuncio walked steadily down the long country road. He didn't go fast and he didn't go slowly. He went just like a man in Paraguay who has many miles to walk and must not get tired too early in the day. Señor Anuncio was dressed in a neat gray suit and he carried a cane in one hand. In the other was a very small grip. Hung from his shoulder was a small pack. His shoes had been bright and shiny when he started, but now they were covered with dust.

The workmen in the fields he passed looked at him with surprise. They could see that he was a city gentleman.

"What is a señor from the city doing here?" they muttered. "It is very unusual for such a person to be walking along the country road. Rich people from the city usually come galloping through on horseback, scattering our poor chickens from the village streets as they go."

So they stared at Señor Anuncio as he went by. But he paid no attention to the stares. He carried his small grip tightly. His bright eyes watched the birds and the little animals that ran from the roadside as he passed.

For several days Señor Anuncio had been walking. He had left his home in the big city, with a pack of small copies of the Gospels hung from his shoulder. He had determined to walk as far as the village of Nogales that he found on his map. Beginning there and walking back through all the villages he had passed, he would read from the Gospels to the people and try to sell as many copies as he could. He was, you see, a colporteur. His business was to try to help as many people as possible to have copies of the Bible, or of different parts of it. On this day he was planning to reach Nogales. He had not much farther to go.

At last he came to the edge of the village for which he was bound. He was sure it must be Nogales, but he had to be certain. He noticed some children playing under a spreading tree.

"Yes, Señor," they said when he questioned them, "the village is Nogales. And you can see the plaza in the center of the village from here. It is a very little village," they added.

Señor Anuncio sat down to rest before going on. The children did not go back to their play. They stood shyly at a little distance and looked at him. They were not used to señores who came walking down the road to their village.

Señor Anuncio smiled at them.

"Would you care to hear a story?" he asked.

"And why not?" The children crowded around. It seemed silly to them that anyone should ask whether or not they wanted to hear a story. They always wanted to hear stories. Since they had no books, the only stories they knew were those that were told to them by older people.

Señor Anuncio sat down on a log. The children gathered around him on the grass.

"Long, long ago," he began. He told them the tales that all children have loved since the time when mothers and fathers and uncles and aunts and grandmothers and grandfathers began telling the stories of the Bible to children.

"Tell us another," begged the children, after Señor Anuncio had told them seven stories.

"One more," he agreed.

This time he told them the story of the selfish son who took his share of his father's money and went away to a faraway place and wasted it all in foolish living.

Señor Anuncio did not see, as he began the story, that an old man had come softly hobbling up behind him and was listening. After the story had been finished, and the children had been sent off to play, the old man finally spoke to him.

"My son has gone to a faraway place, too," he said sadly. "He has gone to the big city. And from what I hear, I am afraid that he, too, is wasting his money foolishly."

"Tell me about him," said Señor Anuncio.

The old father told him. He loved his boy, oh, ever so much. "His mother and I grieve all day and all night. We long for him to come home to us," said the old man. "He left after the sugar harvest, and that is a long time ago. If his heart had inclined him to come back, it would have been long before now." He sighed deeply.

"I will go to the faraway city," thought Señor Anuncio. "I will see what I can do to find that foolish young man." But he did not say anything out loud. He did not wish to raise the old man's hopes.

Señor Anuncio cut short his visit in the country. He went back to the city. He hunted up some people whose names the old father had mentioned. "They were supposed to be friends of my son!" he had said.

"Do you know a young man from the country whose name is Jorge?" asked Señor Anuncio. "He comes from the village of Nogales."

"We used to know him," admitted the friends cautiously. What did this neat little man want? They wondered.

"Used to? Don't you know him now?"

"We have not seen him for months," said the friends.

Then as they saw how worried Señor Anuncio looked, they decided to tell him more. He did not seem to be the sort of person who would get other people into trouble.

"Jorge has been visiting the 'bad hats,'" they said.

"Ah!" said Señor Anuncio. He pursed up his mouth. "That is not good." He knew very well who the "bad hats" were. They were thieves. They made their living through robbery.

Señor Anuncio went to his lodging. He wondered what he should do. At last he had an idea.

He went down into the thieves' part of town. He stood on a street corner. Very quietly he began to speak out loud. He began to tell the story of the Prodigal Son. When he had told it at one street corner, he went on and repeated it at another corner. Sometimes he leaned against a wall in the middle of the block and told the story.

Each time he told it, he thought about the old man down in the country, longing for his boy's return. And, thinking of him, he made the story so full of the father's love and desire to see his boy that even the thieves who listened to it were filled with respect. They took nothing from the pockets of Señor Anuncio.

One dark evening when he had just finished telling the story, a little twist of paper fell at his feet. Someone had dropped it from the window just above him. On it Señor Anuncio read, "Please come up to me."

That message was exactly what Señor Anuncio had been hoping and praying for. He turned and went into the house without stopping to find out whether or not it belonged to the thieves and whether it was dangerous. He hurried upstairs and knocked on the door of the room whose window had been above him.

There on a bed in the room sat a young man, looking very uncertain of himself.

"I heard your story," he said, "and it is about a man like me. I hoped you would come up and talk to me."

"Tell me about yourself," invited Señor Anuncio, sitting down on the bed beside the young man.

"I lived in the country in a small village named Nogales," began the young man. Señor Anuncio's eyes sparkled but he did not interrupt. "I took all the money I made in the sugar harvest and all my father would loan me and I came to the city. I thought I would get rich. But I spent the money in foolish ways. My friends helped me, but when I had no money left, they threw me out." He bowed his head down into his hands and rocked to and fro. "Stupid, stupid that I was!" He waited a moment and then went on. "I was ashamed to go home. My father would be so angry. He might disown me. Better he should think me dead than for me to go home penniless."

Señor Anuncio looked sympathetic, but he asked no questions.

"Tonight," the young man went on, "I heard the story you were telling down there on the street. And the father in the story was not angry. He still loved his son. Do you think," he asked Señor Anuncio, "that there is any chance that my father would welcome me home like the father in the story?"

"Every chance in the world," said Señor Anuncio. "Every chance in the world."

Then he told the young man how he had been at Nogales and how the old father had crept up to listen to the story and had told him how he longed for his son.

"Could it be," asked Señor Anuncio, "that you are that very son?"

The young man got up and straightened his shoulders. He looked Señor Anuncio straight in the eye. "I am. And this very night I will leave here and start back to my father. I will find a job and work hard and prove that I am sorry for my foolishness."

"Good!" said Señor Anuncio. "I am going to give you something that will help you to keep that promise." He took from his pocket a New Testament. "Here, open this."

The book opened to the story of the Prodigal Son, because Señor Anuncio had turned to that place so often. "Read this story. Read other stories from this book. Read the teachings of Jesus. You will come to love him and want to walk in his way."

The young man took the New Testament. "I will read it, I promise you," he said simply.

"Come away from here now," said Señor Anuncio. "I will take you to my lodgings. It is too late to start out upon the road tonight."

In the morning Señor Anuncio set the young man upon his way. "Do not delay upon the road," he urged. "Do not keep that loving father and mother of yours waiting an hour longer than is necessary!"

He watched the young man striding off into the distance.

"What happiness there is going to be in the village of Nogales!" Señor Anuncio said to himself.

16: Four Chickens and Twice Fifty Miles

Africa

THERE was almost no spare money among the people where Bula lived. In his part of Africa men and women traded for what they needed. And as for a boy such as Bula himself, well, what child ever had money?

Bula wandered out to where the goats were pasturing and sat down under a scraggly tree to think.

"Money I must have," he muttered. "It is not well to beg it from my father. Surely anything that is to be given as a gift to the church should be one's own and not the handed-on gift of another."

Up came Walif to get Bula to play. But Bula was not in the mood.

"My heart is troubled by the words of Pastor Moses," he explained, "the words that poured thundering like water in a waterfall from his lips this morning."

"They were strong words," admitted Walif. "In my mind, too, they are still shouting."

"It was news to me," said Bula, "that there are still people in the world without the Bible. I had thought that we were nearly the last people in the world who needed the Bible brought to them."

"I also," agreed Walif. "But Pastor Moses spoke with great sureness. He said that of a certainty there is need for the Bible to go to others."

"The words that trouble me," stated Bula frankly, "are not those. If he said that others need the Bible, it must be so, for Pastor Moses is a person who hates any word that tells a lie. But he also said that we who have been given the Bible—"

"Must pass it on to others," finished Walif. "Those words trouble me also, for the gathering of money to send Bibles is to be made on the next Lord's Day. And shall I pass the coconut shell through my empty hands and let no offering fall from them into it?"

"Shame would come to me to do so!" sighed Bula.

"But there is no money in my hands," went on Walif.

"Nor mine," echoed Bula.

"Nor anything that belongs to me that could be sold," said Walif.

"Not a thing!"

They spent a few gloomy minutes in silence.

"I heard it said about chickens—" began Walif thoughtfully.

"What about chickens?"

"That the chief gives a feast at the end of the month and will buy."

"I have chickens," said Bula hopefully.

"I also."

"Chickens of my own. If I choose to sell two instead of using them to eat on the next feast day, it is of concern to no one but me."

"Or to me about mine. Only—" and Walif looked very, very sober—"it will not be a joyful time when everyone else eats chicken and you and I eat beans."

"No, not very joyful," agreed Bula.

Then he got resolutely to his feet. "Walif, it is not very joyful for people to be without the Bible. If we can each send two chickens' worth of the Bible to those faraway people, we can eat beans and not mind it. At least, not mind it too much."

Walif sprang to his feet. He was always ready to act when there was something to be done.

"What better time than now to catch them?"

The two boys went to the roughly made run where the chickens were kept fenced in with thorny bushes. They decided which ones they could spare.

Then the chase began. To and fro the boys dashed after the chickens. Bula came up with two long tail feathers. Walif held a squawking hen for just a moment before she flapped loose. Both boys were gasping for breath before they succeeded in catching their two fowls each.

They tied the legs of each chicken together with a twist of grass cord and hurried off to the chief's house. But once they arrived there, disappointment awaited them. The chief's cook would not pay what they expected. He offered only a small price.

"Ho! Every boy in the tribe will be bringing us chickens for sale. Is the chief a rich man that he should pay town prices for country chickens? Not one coin more than I have offered you will I pay."

Bula and Walif retired to a shady spot out of hearing to consider the offer.

"Town prices? What are they?"

Bula went to his father to inquire. He came back to report to Walif.

"That is almost twice as much as the chief's cook will pay."

"But the town is fifty miles away."

"This week we are having our holiday from school. We could walk to the town," suggested Walif.

Bula looked unbelieving. "It would take days!"

Walif nodded. "I have an uncle who lives halfway there. We could sleep at his house overnight. And we have walked twenty-five miles in a day often and often."

Bula knew that. He and Walif were strong and were used to long, stiff trips on foot. The whole question was, would the result of the trip be worth the trouble?

"If we sell here at the small price, we two can give four

chickens' worth of Bible to those people," figured Bula slowly. "If we sell in the town we can get twice as much. It will be the same as eight chickens' worth!"

"Let us do it," urged Walif. "Twice as big a gift and the fun of going to town besides!"

"The hard work of going to town, you mean," groaned Bula. "But it will be worth it to double our gift."

So, with permission gained from their parents, they set forth the next day. It was a hard trip, with the chickens to carry and food for the journey as well.

It was easy to sell the chickens in town. The boys received twice as much as the chief's cook had offered. They clinked the coins joyfully in their hands.

The road home seemed easier. The double price for the chickens weighed little. It was securely fastened into the boys' clothing, and their pride was high.

Next Lord's Day came at last. Pastor Moses stood before his people. He reminded them of the need for Bibles in far-away lands.

As the coconut-shell offering plate passed from hand to hand, Bula grinned broadly at Walif. The tinkle of coins sounded forth to the ears of the whole congregation as the boys opened their hands to let the town price of four chickens fall into the shell they held between them.

The whole congregation and Pastor Moses himself smiled at the sound. They knew all about the boys' long trip of twice fifty miles to double their offering. And many were the coins that went into the coconut shell because of the understanding that Bula's and Walif's plan for giving had brought to the people of the village.

17: A Miner Strikes Pay Dirt

United States

HIGH above the little shack of old Jan towered the Rocky Mountains. In winter, snow piled deep around him, and bitter winds howled down the canyons, whipping the evergreens.

Jan, the old miner, did no mining then. When snow was deep he thought of Finland, where he had been born and where his childhood had been spent. He remembered the days when the sun had glittered bright on long stretches of unspotted snow. He thought of the boys and girls speeding down the steep forest slopes on the skiis they loved so much.

On dark winter evenings Jan would remember his Finnish home. He would close his eyes and see once more his sturdy father and his strong, comfortable mother, sitting close by a blazing fire with their children gathered around the fireplace. Jan could almost hear his father reading in his deep, calm voice from the old family Bible.

Jan would go to his chest and open it. He would bring out his one treasure—the big Finnish Bible that his father had given him on the day he left home to come to the New World. By the light of his kerosene lamp Jan would trace out the words. His fingers would follow the printed lines. For companionship he would read out loud, in the Finnish language that his childhood had known, the teachings of Jesus, or the adventures of Paul, or the majestic poetry of the Psalms, or the stories of heroes of Old Testament days.

Somehow, although he could never get to a church, Jan managed to read his Bible and to offer the prayers his mother had taught him. He lived a quiet life, making a bare living at his mining, always hoping to strike "pay dirt," a find of gold or silver or copper that would bring him wealth. But meantime, he was content to be kindly and true and honest in all he did, and helpful to his friends and neighbors.

Jan was far away, up in one of the canyons, where he was hoping to find some kind of mineral, the day his lonely shack took fire. No one was there to save it. When he came back to the clearing, leading his little burro, he stood staring. No shack! Just charred bits of wood! Nothing left of his home or all that he possessed—little though that had been.

At first Jan stared, stunned, hardly able to believe it. Then he rushed forward. His chest! Perhaps by some miracle it had been saved.

But no, there was no trace of it.

Then slow tears began to run down Jan's face. Not for his shack. After all, he could build another one. Not for his blankets and pots and pans. He could buy others with the savings that he had in the bank in the Center, a couple of miles down the mountainside. But for his one treasure he grieved—his Finnish Bible! No one had Finnish Bibles in this country where he lived. His Bible was gone and could never be replaced.

Jan built a new shack and people from the Center who knew the old miner and loved him, brought blankets and pots and pans, and a rough chair or two, and a lamp and a stove.

"Why not?" they said. "After all, old Jan has spent his days in this country, going for aid when someone was snowed in, or chopping wood for a sick neighbor in a lonely clearing, or helping someone with a job that needed two to do it."

So old Jan began life again. Only it was not quite the same. On winter days his thoughts went back with the first white snowfall to his childhood in Finland. But after dark when his lamp was lit there was no Bible to pore over.

"English I cannot read," he would explain to the church

people at the Center who offered to give him a Bible. "Too many are the words that I do not understand. It is not the same. Only in Finnish does the Bible speak to my heart. And Finland is across the ocean and I cannot go there to buy a new Bible."

Whenever Jan went to the Center for supplies he stopped to visit the Blakes. Little Clara Blake was his favorite of all the children in the village. One day as he hitched his burro to the post in front of the house, Clara came dancing out to meet him.

"Jan! Jan! I think I know where you can get a Finnish Bible!" she said. "Look what they gave us in Sunday school today."

Clara had a little booklet in her hand. "See!" she said eagerly as she opened it. "A verse from the Bible, printed in ever so many languages."

Jan took the booklet in his hand. Yes, there were ever and ever so many languages there. Clara leaned against his knee and ran her finger down the page.

"Chinese," she read, "and Japanese and Dutch and Italian!"

They went on through the booklet.

"Ah!" Jan suddenly drew in a long breath. "It is here! It is here!"

He had come to the verse in Finnish and he pored over the familiar words. They said to him in his own old language what they did to Clara in English—"For God so loved the world that he gave his only begotten Son, that whosoever believeth on him should not perish, but have eternal life."

"It is the same! It is just as it was in my Bible," said Jan, with a smile reaching up into his eyes.

Then the smile faded. "But it is only one little verse," he said. "A wonderful verse, but just one."

Clara turned the little booklet over. "Let us write to the

people who made this. Maybe they have all the Bible in Finnish," she suggested to Jan.

It was Clara's mother who wrote the letter.

Clara watched the mail. Day after day she examined the letters that came. At last there was one with "Bible House, New York," in the upper left-hand corner. They kept it carefully for Jan. "Why doesn't he come?" Clara asked day after day.

It was almost a week before Jan came. Clara and her mother and father all stood around while the old man opened the letter.

Yes, a Finnish Bible could be bought, the letter said. It told the price and just how the order should be sent in.

The very next day a letter was in the mail on its way to New York with Jan's money order enclosed.

Not long afterward a package came for old Jan. Clara and her mother and father and all the neighbors gathered around to see the old miner open it. Jan's gnarled old hands were firm as he cut the string and carefully unwrapped the paper. He opened the box that was inside. Clara held her breath.

There it lay—the Holy Bible in the Finnish language.

Old Jan's hands trembled a little now as he lifted it out. He opened it to the *Psalms*, to the Gospel of *Matthew*, to the Book of *Acts*.

"The same! It's just the same! It's all here!" he murmured. Then he looked at the smiling faces all around him.

"All my life I look in the hills for pay dirt," he said, "hoping some day to strike it." He smiled happily. "And here it is! Pay dirt! Worth more than anything I could possibly ever dig out of the mountains!"

He wrapped his treasure up again. Supplies were loaded on the tiny burro. Clara and her mother watched the old man disappear up the trail that led off into the canyon and to his lonely shack.

That night, they knew, old Jan would light his kerosene lamp. He would draw his rough chair close to the table. He would lay his new-old treasure before him and his fingers would trace along line after line of the familiar passages as he read out loud the words he had thought lost to him forever.

18: The Man Who Surprised His Family

Japan

Plum blossom opened her dark eyes in horror. Yes, her father was speaking of Honorable Uncle, and the words that he was saying were hot and angry.

"That drunkard!" The words came out loudly. "Why doesn't he drink himself to death? Then at least he would stop disgracing the family."

Plum Blossom shrank back into the corner. She loved Honorable Uncle. He was kind and gentle and always brought her a toy when he visited their village. True, his face was often rather red and he talked foolishly at such times, but always, always he was gentle with her. How could Honorable Father say such things!

But Honorable Father was not yet through with saying things about his brother. "Drunkard and spendthrift and gambler," he shouted. "Not even the dealers will lend him money, nor give him supplies for his bicycle shop any more. He's a good-for-nothing. A failure!"

Honorable Uncle chose just that time to appear at the door. Plum Blossom rushed to the doorway to greet him. His eyes were clear and sparkling. No disagreeable odor of the rice wine of which he was so fond was anywhere about him. He smiled and patted her shoulder fondly.

His brother scowled. He did not particularly care to have Honorable Uncle coming to his house. Even Honorable Grandmother had ceased looking for him with pleasure. But here he was, and the family gathered to receive him.

When the greetings were over, Honorable Uncle spoke. "I have news you will be glad to hear," he said, just a little nervously. "It is this. I have been reading in a book, and I am become a new person. I am going to live a new life and give up my wine-drinking and gambling. No longer shall I be a disgrace to the family."

Plum Blossom's eyes sparkled. So there! Honorable Father was wrong about Honorable Uncle. She could have sung for happiness.

But her father's lips only curled into a scornful smile. "You! A new life!" he said. "That is a fine story to expect us to believe! Why no power on earth can keep you from the rice wine! A worthless fellow such as you have become can't change!"

Honorable Uncle's face grew pale. He had thought his family would be glad to hear. Instead it was plain that they all agreed with Older Brother, Plum Blossom's father.

Honorable Uncle bowed politely. "May I tell you what has happened?"

"We will listen. But make it short. The babbling tales of drunkards—"

Honorable Grandmother spoke sharply. "Your brother is not drunk. We will listen with attention to his story."

Plum Blossom edged closer on the mat where they all sat on the soft, clean floor.

"Listen then. It is now some time ago that two men stopped to have their bicycles repaired at my shop. As I worked, I talked to them. They were sellers of the books of their religion, and I bought some small booklets that were parts of what they called the Bible. I read those booklets. But they said nothing to my understanding."

Plum Blossom looked sympathetic. They had just started a study in school that said nothing, so far, to her understanding, and she knew how Honorable Uncle felt.

"So when the men came again for more work, I told them that I could not understand the books. They invited me to the inn, saying they would explain the meaning of the teachings." Honorable Uncle flushed. "I went. But first I drank much rice wine, so that I was almost drunk."

His brother muttered something, but Honorable Grandmother's eyes flashed and he said nothing out loud.

"Very patient they were," said Honorable Uncle. "Again and again I went to listen to them. And not once did they reproach me for drinking wine before I came. Verse after verse they read and explained."

Honorable Uncle stopped to think for a moment. "I grew interested. The teachings were good. And one evening they opened the Bible and pointed to a verse and asked me to read for myself. That verse, written in the Book for all to read, can you guess what it said?" Honorable Uncle looked around. No one spoke. "It said, 'Be not drunken with wine!'"

"Ah-h-h!" said Plum Blossom's father.

"Then they spoke to me, and we read more and I decided that I would be a follower of Jesus of whom the Book teaches, and that I would no longer drink rice wine, or gamble, or spend my money in wicked ways."

He looked at his family. But Honorable Father only laughed. "It is a good story. But to carry out a resolve is a different matter. How often have you promised me to drink no longer?"

Honorable Grandmother smiled gently. "To make a resolve is a good thing," she said. "Come back, my son, when you have carried it out. That is a different thing."

Honorable Uncle rose. "I had hoped my news would make you happy," he said sadly.

"It would, if there were any chance of its being true," said his brother shortly.

Only Plum Blossom went clattering softly on her *geta* down to the garden gate with her uncle. "It makes me happy," she said. "I am glad, glad, glad!"

Honorable Uncle's sad eyes became bright again and full

of determination. "You shall have reason, child." And he walked away with a firm stride along the road to town.

Days slipped by one after the other. Winter came and snow with it, and no one went to town for weeks. But one day Honorable Father made the trip and came home looking excited.

"I have been to my brother's," he told Honorable Grandmother, "and his wife tells me a story hard to believe. She says, and she insists upon it, that your son, Honorable Mother, has touched not one drop of rice wine in all these weeks. She says that the money he makes he is storing up. Not once has he visited the gambling house, nor spent his earnings in ways that have distressed us."

"What does *he* say?" eagerly asked Honorable Grandmother.

Plum Blossom hung about waiting for the reply.

"I did not see him. He was away on an errand of work," replied Honorable Father.

"Too hard to believe!" said Honorable Grandmother to herself.

"But, Honorable Grandmother, I believe it," said Plum Blossom softly.

"Do you, child?" Honorable Grandmother sighed. "If only it is true! But never in my life have I heard of a power that would turn a drunkard and a gambler from the evil of his ways. And your uncle—" She sighed.

"But there is also," went on Honorable Father, "trouble in my brother's house. For his credit is worn out, and no one will sell him the great number of things he needs to have in his shop. His stock is low, and with the money he earns he seems only to be able to buy the most necessary parts."

"He owes money on every hand, that I have heard," said Honorable Grandmother. "He even owes the shopkeeper in this village and our neighbors in the next town." She looked sad. Honorable Uncle's behavior had been enough to make any mother sad and any brother ashamed and angry.

More days slipped by. New Year's would soon be here. One morning Honorable Father went to town again.

"I will call on my brother," he said. But he added rather bitterly, "Only, I suppose he will not be at home. This is the time of paying debts and he usually skips out so that no one will be able to find him and ask for the money that he owes them."

But Honorable Father was mistaken. Honorable Uncle was at home, his shop clean and shining, his face happy and serene, and his family preparing for New Year's.

They greeted Plum Blossom's father with joy. "See," said Honorable Uncle, "I have been out and have collected money that people owed me. And with what I have saved, I am starting out to pay at least something to every person to whom I owe money. I shall ask each one to be patient till I can pay the whole amount."

Honorable Father looked at his brother in amazement. "It must be that I was wrong," he said softly. "It must be that something has happened that I thought was impossible."

Honorable Uncle led his brother to the window. "Yes," he said, "impossible! But God can do what is impossible, and through his Word he has led me away from the rice wine and the gambling." He pointed to a beautiful little box in the window of his shop. The box was open and in it lay the New Testament and other little booklets about Christian teaching.

"God's Word showed me a new way. I put it in the window so people may ask about it," he said.

Plum Blossom's father looked earnestly at his brother. Then his face broke into a smile. "This time I believe you," he said. "Even I can see that you have changed. I shall hurry home and tell our mother. No gift on New Year's could make her so happy. And as for little Plum Blossom," he added, "she has always had faith in you. Her feet will dance from one room to another when she hears of your welfare."

The two brothers started out into the snow together. "I shall walk home with you. I have a debt to pay to the shop-keeper in your village. And I will call upon our Honorable Mother and upon little Plum Blossom," said Honorable Uncle.

There were light hearts in Plum Blossom's family that night. Honorable Father pulled from his pocket a little book-let. "We also shall read from God's Word," he said. "For if there is in this world a power that can make what your honorable uncle was, Plum Blossom, into what he is today, I, too, must learn of it."

"Truly, it is a marvel," nodded Honorable Grandmother. "Now read, my son, and we will listen with our hearts as well as our ears."

Plum Blossom was very quiet as for the first time in all her life she heard words from the Bible. It was the story of Jesus and the children that Honorable Uncle had marked for them to read, thinking of Plum Blossom.

"I wish," thought Plum Blossom, "that I could see Jesus. I want to hear more about him."

19: Teresa's Great Big Holy Book

Mexico

WHAT is the trouble, Mamacita?" asked Consuela.

Mamacita didn't answer. Not at first at least. She just sat, rocking herself to and fro, looking worried.

Consuela crept closer. Her mother was so seldom sad that she felt frightened. In all the villages of this part of Mexico no one was so gay, even when there was trouble, as the mother of Consuela. But now she was not even answering when spoken to.

Consuela looked at her father. "What is it that troubles. Mama?" she whispered.

Papa frowned. "It is a bad business," he said. "The priest has told us that we must buy the big Holy Book that he has for sale."

Consuela looked surprised. "But holy books are for priests. They are not for poor people like us."

Then Mama spoke. "He says it is a holy book. He says that if we buy it, it will save our souls."

Papa growled out, "So he says! But to my mind his reason for selling is that he needs the money. Always he is in need of money. He is not a good priest, that one. He has no care for his people. Why should we buy the book?"

But Mama looked frightened. "But listen, Chico. We must do what the priest says. If not, evil may befall us. I am full of fear to refuse."

Papa looked unhappy. "I also. But look you, Teresa. We have no such large amount of money. To buy that book we must sell part of our land. How shall we live if we sell our land?"

So Papa refused to buy the great big Holy Book from the

priest, and Mama wept and was afraid. Consuela felt un-happiness in the air whenever she came into the house and no one had any comfort in living. Even the fiesta brought no gaiety to the house of Consuela.

Every week, when Consuela and Mama went to the church to put before the shrine a bunch of the lovely little flowers-of-the-Virgin, the priest spoke to them about buying the great big Holy Book. He was not pleased because Mama said that Chico, Consuela's papa, would not buy.

That priest was not a good priest. He did not love his people. He did nothing for them and thought only of his own good. How Consuela wished that the priest of her uncle's village were here instead of this one! He would never ask that a man sell his land to buy a book he could not read.

Then came sickness to the village. Many died. And of those who died one was Chico. Teresa and Consuela mourned with the other sad ones of the village. And the priest who was hungry for the money that he could get, so that he could make a pleasure trip, said coldly to Mama, "If you had bought the Holy Book, this might not have happened."

Then Mama, frightened lest she might die also and leave Consuela without a home, sold part of the land that Chico had left her and bought the Book. She did not know that buying or not buying a book had nothing to do with sick-ness and dying.

The priest brought the Book and laid it upon the chest in the adobe house where Teresa and Consuela lived all alone, and pretended to give them a blessing. Because they had been frightened, they felt comforted.

One day Uncle Pedro came riding up on his prancing horse. He had borrowed it from the Señor who owned the ranch upon which he worked.

"There was need I should come and see how the world

treats you, my sister," he said, greeting her with affection and holding Consuela in his arms lovingly. "There is room in our house for you, if you should so wish."

But Mama said no. She and Consuela would stay here on what was left of their land and try to make a living from it.

Then she told Uncle Pedro about the great big Holy Book that she had bought from the priest. She showed it to him, lying upon the chest, with no one to read it or to tell what it was about.

Uncle Pedro sniffed with scorn. "An easy way to make money," said he. "Frightening a woman to death and then taking part of her land! Ah well, it is done now. Let us see what is in this book that makes it so holy."

He opened the Book where it lay and began to read. The words were strange to all of them. Uncle Pedro could not read very well, but he stumbled along. " 'In the beginning God created the heavens and the earth,' " he read. And on and on.

Neither he nor Teresa nor Consuela knew that it was the Bible they were reading, for never before had it been read to them. Nor had the lazy priest told them the stories from it. As for Uncle Pedro, he had had no use at all for church and never went near it in his own village.

"It is good reading," said Uncle Pedro after a while. "I must go now, but I shall come again, and we shall read some more."

Whenever Uncle Pedro came he read from the great big Holy Book. Slowly and with difficulty he read. Sometimes they could understand the meaning. But often the reading was just words that went in at the ears but never reached the mind.

"Even so," said Teresa, contentedly, "if the book is holy, only good can come from reading it."

Consuela found happiness in those days. Mama felt happier, too. It was the season of gardens and there was enough to eat. She did not spend too much time thinking of the winter when they might be hungry.

One day Consuela went skipping through the high-walled, unpaved streets of her village. She was going to play with Trini, who lived at the other end of the ranch. But suddenly she stopped. Singing was coming from behind the patio wall of one of the houses.

Singing was something that Consuela loved above anything else. And this singing was of a tune that was new to her. It was a man singing!

Consuela slipped into the patio. She knew the family well and was always welcome. Even the great fierce dog, Temeroso, the Timid One, as he was called for a joke, did no more than look sternly at her as she came in.

The family were gathered around a stranger. A bicycle was propped up against the wall beside him and he was singing. When the singing was done, he took a small book from his pack. He opened it and read.

Consuela gasped. The words were the very same that Uncle Pedro had read from the great big Holy Book no longer ago than last week.

Consuela's flying feet carried her home, and soon her mother was hurrying back with her to the house where the reading was going on.

They got there in time to hear the stranger explain what the words meant. He talked in plain language and seemed to know all about how village people lived. The words that had had little meaning before became alive and seemed to speak to their hearts.

Then he sang again. And because the children who had gathered around were looking eagerly at him, he sang a song for children, and even took time to teach them to sing it. It was a song that said that Jesus loves each one and that the Bible tells us so. He opened the book again and read about Jesus welcoming the children.

"This book is part of the Bible," he said. "The Bible is God's Book. It tells us about him. It tells us how to live as his children."

When he was ready to go, the stranger said, "I should like to come every week to read and to sing and to teach you about God's love. Shall I be welcome?"

Then the woman of the house said, "Señor, the words you have read and spoken and the singing you have done are good. You will be welcome."

The stranger wheeled his bicycle out of the patio, past Temeroso, who growled deep in his shaggy white throat, and got ready to leave.

"God be with you all," he called.

"God go with you, Señor," chorused all the people who had come to the gate.

Consuela and her mother had much to tell Uncle Pedro the next time he came. They repeated what the stranger had said about the meaning of the words. Uncle Pedro found those words and read them again. Then Consuela begged him to find the story about Jesus, but although he looked and looked he could not find it. "Ask the man to come to this house and put a paper at the right place," he said.

Week and week after week the stranger came to the village. Soon he was not a stranger but a friend to everyone. Some, it is true, did not welcome him. "Those Evangelicals," they would mutter, for that is what Methodists and Presbyterians and members of other Protestant churches are called in Mexico. "The priest would not like his being here. When he returns he will be angry if you listen to the stranger."

But Teresa only smiled. "The Evangelical reads from the same Book that the priest sold to me," she said. "The priest told me that it would bring me God's message. And truly I think that he was right."

Week after week, Teresa and Consuela and others listened to the reading of the Bible by the visiting Señor Pastor. For that is what he was, the Señor Pastor of an Evangelical church in a near-by town. They heard his teaching. They learned to sing the hymns.

Best of all they came to love the Lord Jesus, and upon a day Teresa and Consuela and one or two others were baptized and became Evangelical Christians. So a little Evangelical church was started in that ranch village.

The one who had been their priest never came back. And although a visiting priest of the Catholic Church came and spoke angry words, Teresa had always an answer ready for them.

"Do not be angry," she would say. "The Bible we bought at a great price from the very hands of our own priest, and all we do is to follow its teachings."

One day Consuela, who was learning to read in the new village school, begged her mother to learn also. "It is not hard, Mamacita! I shall teach you."

Her mother only laughed comfortably. "I have enough to do without learning to read. And why should I, when every child in the village can read to me?"

One day she added, quietly but with determination, "See you, my Consuela, your mother is only a poor ranch woman who cannot read or write. But you shall learn, and when you have finished the school here, you shall go to the city and learn more. Some day, if it pleases the good God, you will come back here and be the village teacher. On Sundays and in the evenings you will help our little church to understand better the teachings of the great big Holy Book. You will help our village to be truly Christian."

Consuela's eyes opened wide in astonishment. Surely such

a thing was impossible! But if Mama wished it, she would work hard to make it happen.

"Truly," said Mama, "the buying of that great big Holy Book was wise. For our souls and for our lives it has been good. Now run along and play. For the Señor Pastor said only last week that strong bodies are needful for those who would do God's work."

Consuela skipped away to run and visit Trini. The children were making a play of one of the Bible stories to surprise the Señor Pastor the next time he came.

20: Follow the Line

United States

Jimmy sat on the front seat with his father. "Keep your eye on Uncle John's car. We're going to trail it all the way from North Carolina to Indianapolis," said his father. "It's when other cars cut in, or we get stopped by a traffic light that you'll need to watch out for it most carefully."

Jimmy wriggled with pleasure. He had been looking forward to the trip for weeks. He and his parents were riding in their own car. Uncle John and Aunt Net had two ladies from the church in their car. They were going to a convention at Indianapolis. What fun the trip was going to be!

It was just when the sun was hottest on the first afternoon that the back left tire went flat. Jimmy's father honked loudly—two long, a short, and a long. That was the signal to the car ahead that the back car was in trouble.

Uncle John's car slowed to a stop and backed along the country road to the spot where Jimmy's father was already busy with his tire tools.

"What luck!" he said.

"Yes, but we are in luck in where it happened," said Jimmy's father cheerfully. "Right under a row of tall shade trees."

The men got to work. The women decided to sit in the shade while the tire was changed.

"I'm thirsty," said Uncle John. He straightened up and looked around. Back from the road was a cottage and on its porch was sitting a white-haired Negro woman with a big book in her lap.

"Run up and ask for drinking water, Jimmy," said his uncle.

Jimmy climbed the steep slope to the cottage. The old woman turned her face toward him but said never a word.

Jimmy came to the steps. "Please," he said, "we've a flat tire, and we're thirsty. Could we get a drink of water?"

The woman smiled. "Water? The best spring water in the world. Just follow this line, Sonny, and you will come to it. It's over the little hill and down in the woods." She laid her hand on a stout cord that was tied to the porch pillar. It ran across the yard and vanished among the trees and bushes.

Jimmy thanked her and followed the cord. It led him to a cool, deep spring. Jimmy drank and drank. He called to the others then, and they came to him through the woods with cups and each drank all he wanted to.

"I'll go back with you," said Jimmy's father. "I want to ask some directions. And we must thank the old woman for the water."

They went softly through the dim, cool woods and across the yard with its sweet-scented flowers. "I've never been in a yard that smelled so sweet. Whoever lives here must specialize in flowers that have plenty of fragrance," remarked Jimmy's father.

As they came to the cottage his eyes lighted up with understanding. The old woman was still sitting there, but she was not seeing them. She seemed to be looking far over the hills, but her eyes were not seeing anything at all. Her lips were moving. Her fingers were moving, too. They were moving slowly across the pages of the great book she held in her lap—across the tiny raised dots of the Braille Bible for the blind.

"She's blind!" whispered Jimmy's father. "That's what the cord is for—to guide her to the spring. And that's why sweet-scented flowers are planted. She can't see them but she can enjoy them."

The old woman heard the whispering. Her ears were sharp even though she could not see.

"Did you find the water, Sonny? Tastes good on a hot day like this, doesn't it?"

"Yes, we did, and it was good, all right."

Jimmy's father spoke. "We are much obliged." He hesitated. "Is there anything we could do for you?"

The old woman beamed. "No, thank you. Nothing at all. You can see that my eyes don't do me any good. Been blind like this ever since I was a child. But I don't need help. Not me!" And she chuckled cheerfully.

"You don't live here alone!" Jimmy's father exclaimed.

"Sure do! And I like it! My son fixed me the lines. Line to the water spring. Line to my chicken house. Line to the apple tree. Line to my vegetable garden. And inside the house I can find my own way about." She smiled at them, although she could not see them. "I just follow my lines." Then she lifted the great Book in her hands. "Travelers, do you know what this is?"

"It's in Braille," said Jimmy's father. "And I rather think it's the Bible!"

"Just so! Just so! Listen to an old woman, Traveler. It's easy to find my spring of water with that line you followed. It's just as easy to reach heaven and peace with this line."

She laid her hand on the line to the spring. "Line here to water." She touched the line that went the other way to the garden. "Line here to food." Then she laid her hand lovingly on the Bible. "Line here to God. All my life is lived by lines, Traveler. And this line here is the most important of them all."

"I don't live my life by cords to the spring and to the garden," said Jimmy's father, gently, "but I do try to live it by the line of the Bible. And so do those who are traveling with me today."

"That's good! That's good!" The old woman beamed again.

Jimmy's father and the old woman talked on for a few moments. Then Uncle John shouted to them to hurry, and they said good-by. Jimmy's father forgot all about the directions he was going to ask.

The old woman stood up on her porch, firm and dignified. Her face was turned toward the sound of their footsteps going down her pathway. She waited till she heard the engines roar and then soften to a purr before she shouted down to them, "Follow the line, Travelers! Always follow the line!"

Jimmy turned wondering eyes to his father. "She didn't seem sad because she was blind," he said.

"No. She isn't sad. She's learned a lesson that most of us don't know the ABC's of. She's learned that it's the lines that matter."

They rolled down the road. As they went down, down into the valley, they almost seemed to hear the strong, confident voice of the old woman coming to them again, "Follow the line, Travelers! Always follow the line!"

21: Singers in the Dark

Peru

PEOPLE were gathering for market day in the little town of Tayabamba. High over their heads soared a condor. Its great wings spread out as it swept between them and the blue peaks of the Andes. All about them lay the great mountains towering into the sky.

On the trail, a thousand feet above the village, a traveler paused as he caught sight of the little town in the deep valley below him. It was Renoso. He was only a *peón*, a day laborer, but his eyes sparkled with pleasure at the scene before him. "It is a good land, this Peru of ours," he thought to himself.

He started on down the trail to the village. It wasn't much more than that. Those who could, used mules for traveling. Renoso's mules were his own two sturdy legs. He had no mule to carry him on his journeys. Nevertheless he was happy. He was going home across the mountains from a job of work he had been doing in another valley. He carried his earnings, his Bible, his hymnbook, and a copy of the church magazine, *Renacimiento*. Renoso was a good member of the Evangelical church, as the Protestant church is called in South America. He would need those things in the church back home just as much as he had when away from home.

Market was still going on when he reached the little town of Tayabamba. Renoso was pleased. He had been traveling the lonely trail. Now he could enjoy the bustle and gaiety of the weekly market. He could buy a present, maybe, to take to his mother. He could talk to people of all sorts. Renoso was a friendly fellow. There was nothing he liked better than a bit of conversation.

He found them ready enough to talk, the villagers and those from other little settlements who had come to sell their wares at Tayabamba. Some were still busy at their stalls. Others were packing up to go home. Still others were hurrying up the steps of the big, old Catholic church to take an offering and to burn a candle at the shrine of a saint, before starting home.

"Will you not buy a candle to burn?" asked the candle-man, at his booth outside the church.

"No," said Renoso, easily. "I do not burn candles. Our family is of the Evangelicals. We study the Bible and have worship with hymns. There is no candle-burning before the shrines of our church." With that he pulled out his Bible.

The curious people had never seen a Bible, and Renoso showed it and read a story or two from its pages.

"A good book!" remarked Big Uncle.

"Perhaps the priest has a copy," suggested Old Grandfather. "He might read it to us if we asked him."

"I do not believe he would." Renoso knew it was very unlikely.

"Sell us your Bible, then. I would have more of it," urged Big Uncle.

"Not I! It was given me on a very special day. See"— Renoso opened it to the front—"my name in big letters and the date. I could not part with it!"

Renoso stayed that night at the inn. Big Uncle and Old Grandfather and Little Crooked, the cripple, and others gathered around him. They liked Renoso. They wanted to hear more of his travels and of his church.

"This worship," said Big Uncle. "You say you sing?"

"That we do, Señor!" agreed Renoso. "Hymns of praise to God, and hymns of prayer for help and guidance."

"Sing us one," said Little Crooked.

"Ah, yes, sing us one," they all begged.

Renoso looked around to see whether they were joking. He was no singer! How could he sing?

But the faces around were eager. "I have not the voice," said he, with hesitation. Then seeing their disappointment, he made up his mind. "Well, I shall sing. But you, too, must join me. I shall teach you the hymn."

Renoso sang. He sang of the love of God and gave praise for his goodness. It was a simple song, with easy words and an easy tune. It was one that all the children in Renoso's church learned and sang sweetly.

Stumblingly at first and then with greater assurance the folk around him followed the words and the tune. Old Grandfather's voice cracked and quavered. Big Uncle boomed out on the wrong notes. But Little Crooked had an ear for music. Almost as though he had known it all his life he sang, his voice rough but true. Again and again the song was repeated. The women sitting in the dark corners of the room joined in. The children curled up, listening as their parents lifted their voices.

"Leave us your Bible," Old Grandfather begged again and again.

"No," Renoso was firm. "That I cannot do. But I shall leave you my hymnbook, and I shall leave you this magazine of my church. It is called *Renacimiento*—'Being Born Again.' That is what happens when one becomes a follower of Jesus. One becomes a new person, as if one were born anew."

Next morning Renoso started down the trail toward his home town.

He wondered what would happen in that village. He wished that the Señor Pastor of his church could come to it. But Tayabamba was much too far away for that. It would take the Señor Pastor four days of travel to reach it. There were many towns and villages that were nearer the church than Tayabamba where the gospel message had not yet been preached.

Back in Tayabamba, no one was thinking about any Señor Pastor. They had a hymnbook and a magazine. After work those who were interested gathered in Big Uncle's house, and Little Crooked read. He read the words of the hymn they had learned, for Renoso had marked the page. They sang it again and again.

Then slowly, picking out word after word, Little Crooked read other hymns to them. No one else in the group could read as well as he—some not at all. They learned with their ears.

He read what was printed in *Renacimiento*. Some of it was beyond understanding. It spoke of things about which they knew nothing. But some things they could see had to do with those matters of which Renoso had spoken.

"How can we sing the other hymns?" asked Old Woman. "This tune that Renoso taught us, it will not go with the other words."

It was true. They had tried to sing several other hymns to the tune, and there was no way at all by which the notes could be fitted to the words.

"We will make our own tunes," answered Little Crooked firmly. "The words will teach us how to sing them."

One day, while reading in *Renacimiento*, Little Crooked came to the advertisement of the bookstore of the Evangelical churches in Peru. It was called the Inca Bookstore and it was in Lima, the capital of the country. He found there the name of the very hymnbook they had in their village. It was for sale, for a certain amount of money! To his great excitement, he found that Bibles, too, were for sale! Bibles just like Renoso's! He hurried to Old Grandfather and Big Uncle with his discovery.

That night there was much calculation. In the end a letter

went to Lima, to the bookstore, ordering a few Bibles, hymn-books, and some other things.

The people in the bookstore were puzzled. There were, so far as they knew, no Evangelical Christians in Tayabamba. It was a little Catholic village, far from any Evangelical church. But they filled the order promptly and put it in the mail. "Tayabamba," they would say to themselves, once in a while. "I wonder who it is that wants Bibles and hymnals there."

The package arrived in the village after a while, brought up the trail, with all the other mail, on the back of a mule. Others beside the faithful learners gathered to see the package opened. The rejoicing few did not notice the frowns on the faces of the village leaders at finding that Big Uncle and Little Crooked and Old Grandfather and Old Woman and others in the little town had Protestant Bibles and hymn-books. They were too full of joy at having Bibles like Renoso's to see that everyone else was not as happy about it as they.

With Bibles and hymnbooks in their hands the poor read-ers began to get practice in reading and before long they could do much better. They had to read in Spanish and not in their own Indian language, but most of them knew some Spanish anyway, and they soon learned more.

"See," said Big Uncle, "here in this magazine it speaks of gathering the children and teaching them. Why should we not do so? This learning of hymns and studying the Bible should be a part of every child's teaching. Let us have a school for the children."

So a little Sunday school was started. But alas! The word "school" was used all by itself. And from that came trouble —serious trouble. The Catholic priest of that small village did not want anyone to become an Evangelical. He thought of a plan to stop what was going on.

"Ha!" said he. "So they will start a school! These ignorant

people will start a school and teach the religion of the Evangelicals! It is not legal to start schools!"

That was true enough. To start a school, permission would have to be secured. Big Uncle and Little Crooked did not know that. Nor did they know that to start a *Sunday* school no such permission was necessary.

"Why not put an end to this Evangelical teaching in our village?" the priest suggested to the village leaders. "Just throw Big Uncle and Old Grandfather and Little Crooked and a half a dozen of the other men into jail for a few days and the trouble will come to an end."

And so it was done.

"What now!" said Big Uncle, when they had recovered enough from surprise to say anything at all.

What indeed! Here they were, crowded into one, single, filthy room, with three-quarters of the floor covered with the water that dripped from the damp walls.

One tiny window, high up above them, let in very little light. The great wooden door with its heavy bars was tightly locked.

The womenfolk were allowed to bring bundles of straw and mats for their menfolk to sleep on. They could bring food to them once a day. But the door stayed locked and no one knew what was to happen to the prisoners. There was nothing for them to do all day long.

One day went by. And another.

"Let us send a telegram to the bookstore in Lima. Perhaps those people who sell Bibles can send someone to help us," suggested Little Crooked daringly.

"It seems a wild thing to do, but we have no other friends," Old Grandfather muttered softly, as his old bones groaned from the damp walls and floor.

It was Old Grandmother who tramped to the next town to send the wire. "It would be best not to send it from here.

I will go to market tomorrow and the message will go from there," she said.

The third day came and went.

"We shall be here for some time," decided Little Crooked. "Let us make some new tunes."

So, to the amazement of the jailer, the merry sound of singing came forth from the dark room where the prisoners sat. They sang, one after another, in joyful praise, all the hymns they knew.

Then Little Crooked and the others took the words of new hymns that they had been learning, and together they made up tunes to fit them.

In between they talked cheerfully and planned what they would do when they were let out.

There was one sad day, when word came that the sick wife of one of the men had died. The others comforted the husband as well as they could and begged the jailer to allow him to leave the prison for the day.

"Allow a prisoner to go free!" The jailer sniffed in surprise at such an idea. "But what is to prevent him from running away?"

"He will come back. It is only that he may go and bury his wife," said Big Uncle.

The jailer looked around at the group of men. "Never in the world would I have supposed I would even listen to such an absurd request," he grumbled. "Well, then, he may go. Though why I trust you is more than I know."

The great door opened and the sad husband slipped out. Evening came and he presented himself at the door of the prison.

"I thank you most gratefully, Señor," he said simply to the jailer. "It was a great comfort to my son and daughter that I might be there."

The jailer blinked his puzzled eyes. Certainly he had trusted the man to come back, and yet he would not have been too surprised had he run off. "This new teaching of yours!" he said under his breath. "What does it do to a man? To make him come back to prison of his own accord!"

A week went by. Two weeks. "Never," said Little Crooked with enthusiasm, "would we have learned so many hymns if we had been busy at our usual work. The time is well spent." He stood in the wettest corner of the room, where a ray of light from the high window fell on his hymnbook. "Now here is a hymn that is a prayer. It asks God for courage. And most certainly we need courage and patience. God only knows whether we are to spend the rest of our lives in this dark hole."

His voice rose up in reverent song.

The jailer spoke earnestly to the village elders gathered about him.

"I tell you, Señores, we had better let them go. My ears are weary with these everlasting Evangelical songs. And the other prisoners are getting ideas. Also the teachings in the songs are gaining in favor. Besides which, one cannot keep men in prison forever for no real reason."

The village elders scowled. They, too, had been disturbed by the singing. The wall of the prison was becoming a loafing place. The singers in the dark were attracting attention.

"Well, then, let them out."

The jailer did not wait. He sprang to his feet and rushed toward his prisoners, drawing the heavy iron key to the barred door from his chain.

"Free, you are free!" he called. "Señores, you are free to go home." He flung the door open. "There is no longer a charge against you. Go!" He was all smiles, for he had come to admire the cheerful prisoners. "Go! God go with you!"

Happy were the homes of Big Uncle and Old Grandfather and Little Crooked and the others that evening. The entire group gathered together in Big Uncle's house. There they sang, as they had sung in the dark, the praises of God. There they rejoiced that the days of their captivity were over.

One day, very soon after, a mule with an American Señor Missionary from Lima came into the village. The telegram to the bookstore had been received. As soon as possible the rescuer had started on his way.

He had not known what he could do, and he was more than relieved to find that the affair was over. Now he could spend his time on more important things.

"There are thirty people here who are reading the Bible. We want to know better how to follow our Lord Jesus," said Little Crooked. "More than thirty are listening to the teaching."

So for a space of days, the Señor Missionary stayed in Tayabamba, helping these new Evangelicals to understand better the teachings of Jesus, and telling them of the world-wide Protestant church of which they were a small part. Then after giving his blessing to them, he rode away.

One by one there were added to the Bible-reading church in Tayabamba those who believed, until they were counted not by the tens but by the hundreds.

"It is a queer thing," the jailer sometimes thinks to himself, "how there is less drinking, less fighting, less crime in this place since the days when those prisoners of mine, jailed for no just cause, sang bravely in the dark. May God be ever with them!"

22: Two Gunmen and a Bible

United States

SAM JOHNSON was a colporteur. He carried Bibles from one part of the countryside to another and he interested people in buying them. There were not many Negro colporteurs and Sam found a ready welcome in the humble homes of the Negro people of North Carolina. Of course, they couldn't often buy a whole Bible, but they did buy many copies of the separate books of the Bible and often took a New Testament.

Sam had an old car in which he traveled around. He had his Bibles and Gospels and New Testaments packed neatly in boxes and stored in the car, so that he wouldn't have to go back too often to get a fresh supply. He could carry some foodstuff too, so that when he found himself at lunchtime or at dinnertime far from where he could buy a meal he just dipped into his supplies and had a picnic by himself beside the road.

One day Sam was in a lonely mountain section with heavy woods and thickets all around him. He knew it would be very late if he followed the highway to the next place where he could get food. Besides, he had been working very hard and he was tired.

So he ran the car down a little side road. A couple of miles from the highway he came to a sort of clearing where there had once been a house. The building was gone now, and only the old cellar-hole, grown full of bushes, was left. But there was a roadway where he could pull off and onto the weedy level space.

"A good place for a picnic," he said to himself. So out he got and ate his lunch. Then he sat down on a big rock with his back leaning up against a tree. He closed his eyes, just for a moment, and dozed off.

Some sound awakened him, and he opened his eyes sleepily. And in that instant Sam was wider awake than he had ever been in his life. Two men were standing in front of him. One had a gun pointed right at him.

"Get up quick, you!"

Sam leaped to his feet. The men looked like ugly customers.

"Open those boxes you have in the car! And don't make any noise about it or you are a dead man!"

Sam got his boxes open quicker than he had ever managed before. And one of them had a hard fastening, too!

The second man came up to the car. "Stand back there!"

Sam stood back. He wasn't arguing about anything. Not anything at all.

The man with the gun kept him covered and watched him closely. The other dipped into box after box. "Well, what do you know!" he exclaimed at last.

"What's the fellow got?" asked the first man impatiently.

"Bibles! Nothing but Bibles! Never saw so many Bibles in my life!" came the answer.

"Bibles!" The first man echoed the word in disgust. Then he spoke to Sam. "You sell Bibles?"

"Yes, sir! Yes, sir!"

The man hesitated, then he dropped the gun to his side. "What's your name? We aimed to kill you."

"Sam, sir." Sam picked up a little courage. The man said *aimed*, not *aim*. And the gun was not pointed right at him any more.

The man went on speaking. "Well, Sam, as I said, we'd aimed to kill you. Just got away from a job of work we did. And we're making for Florida. Need a car. So when we saw you sitting there by the tree, dozing so easy like, we aimed to take the car away from you, get rid of you, and make a getaway!"

His companion was looking at his leader with astonishment. What had come over him? Why not do as they had planned instead of telling this foolish, careless, sleep-in-the-woods Negro about what they had planned to do? Weren't they still going to do it?

The leader moved over to the car. He picked up a Bible.

"Odd thing you should be selling Bibles, Sam. Haven't seen a Bible for years and years." He opened the Book and flicked over the pages. "I had a mother—she was a good woman. Yes, she was a good woman. She taught me the Bible. Haven't thought much about it since she died. Had a good teacher, too. She used to read it to us."

The second man sat down on a fallen tree. He couldn't understand what was going on, but after all, his part in the "little job" had been small. He should worry whether or not they made a getaway.

"Let me look at it again." The leader leafed through the Bible, leaning against the side of the car. "It makes me remember—"

There was silence. The sunlight drifted down through the big trees and flickered over the weed-grown clearing. It rested on watchful Sam, on the revolver laid carelessly on the hood of the car, and on the criminal so busy reading once more words that he had loved when he was a child.

Sam saw the man's hand go up and rub across his eyes. He saw the tears that some old memory had brought to the surface.

Sam slipped to his knees. He was used to doing that when he prayed, and he felt like praying now—praying for God's guidance for the man who was remembering the time when he walked on the roadway of right and truth and honesty and justice. Perhaps he would take that roadway again.

Quiet lay over the clearing. At last the man looked up. His companion was deep in thought. Sam was still kneeling, his eyes closed and his lips moving in prayer.

"Say a prayer for me, Sam." The man's voice was almost gentle. "I need all the prayers a man can get. And then get into your car and go on your way."

His companion started to interrupt, but the leader stopped him. "We have a price on our heads, we two, I imagine, if that man back upstate died." He swallowed hard, as if he found it difficult to put into words what he was thinking. "I've been remembering—remembering what my mother taught me, and my teacher, too. Even though men are putting a price on our heads, Christ can put a promise in our hearts." He smiled a rather sober smile at Sam. "Don't worry! You won't find me with a gun in my hands again. See!" He tossed his weapon deep among the bushes that had grown up in the cellar-hole of the vanished house. "Better be going on, Sam. And don't forget to say a prayer for us. Might be we could become honest citizens again."

Sam climbed into his car. He started the engine and drove slowly out of the rough clearing. As he turned on to the abandoned road he glanced over at the two men.

They were sitting on the fallen tree together now. The leader was reading. The words came to Sam clearly through the afternoon quiet of the deep woods.

" 'Ho, everyone that thirsteth, come ye to the waters, and he that hath no money; come ye, buy . . . without price.' "

"They will take the right road. They will find a way to become honest citizens again." Sam somehow felt very sure of it.

He sang softly as he drove back to the highway and on to his destination.

PART III: INCIDENTS ABOUT THE BIBLE

I: Singing the Bible

Africa

THE hot sun of Africa shone down on the village church. The people were gathered for worship and were singing lustily. In the congregation this Sunday were the evangelists who preached in the neighboring villages.

The hymns they were singing were Christian hymns, but the words and tunes had come to them with the missionaries who first brought Christian teaching to that country. They did not sound in the least like African music.

"I wish we had some truly African hymns," said Mr. James, the missionary. "The spirituals from America that the Negro slaves created are more nearly African than anything else that we sing in church, but even they are not African tunes."

After the service was over, Mr. James spoke to his evangelists about it. Most of the evangelists had a Bible name in addition to their own African one.

Abraham curled his toes around a piece of wood and thought heavily for a few moments. "No, Bwana. We have no worship songs that could be used in Christian worship. We have only the old African chants. They would not do."

Peter and Methuselah and Joshua all said the same. They were quite firm about it. In fact, they were rather shocked at the idea of singing in church to the tunes of old Africa. Church seemed to call for the hymn tunes that had come to them along with Christian teaching from the missionaries.

Every time Mr. James asked, he got the same reply. No songs could be sung to the old African tunes. There were none. At last he gave up trying.

The time of year came for Mr. and Mrs. James to go out along the forest paths into the far villages to visit the evangelists and see how they were getting along in their teaching. How delighted were those teachers, far, far from the churches in the mission stations, to have a visit from the missionaries and to be able to talk with them! How they needed advice on their problems and difficulties! And how proudly they had the village children read and write and recite parts of the Bible for the honored guests!

One day the travelers came to where Evangelist Abraham was living and teaching. Many were the greetings that passed among them. Then everyone sat down to talk.

At first the children sat around the edges of the grown-up crowd to listen, but soon they got tired of conversation about what they didn't understand at all. They slipped off and began one of their dancing-singing games. They sang gaily and clapped their hands joyfully as they stamped their feet and danced.

Mr. and Mrs. James pricked up their ears and began to listen.

"I have heard good news today!"

"Oh! Who told you?"

"God's Word!"

"Christian, oh, who told you?"

"God's Word!"

The children sang on and on.

"Abraham—" Mr. James interrupted the conversation—"that is exactly what I have been asking for! There it is! An old, old African tune, but the words are Christian words."

Abraham looked surprised. "Is that what you meant? But Bwana, that is nothing but an old tune that everyone knows.

We often make up verses about the Bible and verses telling the Bible stories and fit them to that tune. The children love to sing the Bible stories, and so I have arranged many of them for them. But I did not understand that that was what you wanted."

Abraham called the children closer. "Come," he said, "and sing for our guests the verses that tell the story of Jesus blessing the children." Abraham turned to Mr. and Mrs. James. "The children made up these words themselves," he said proudly.

So the children clapped and stamped and danced with joy as they sang the Bible stories they had made into songs, according to the well loved pattern of their own African songs.

When they had finished and had gone off to play, Abraham said thoughtfully, "We already sing through the Ten Commandments in school here. We sing all the stories of Jesus' life that the children know. Sometimes I let them make up the verses. Perhaps those verses are not quite clear, but most of them are good." He smiled. "They go home and sing the stories at home. And do you know, Bwana, people who wouldn't come near our Christian preaching are coming to me privately? They ask me about this good news about which they hear their children singing songs."

Mr. and Mrs. James were delighted. They had found what they were looking for.

When they went back to the mission station, they carried with them the old African tune with its new Christian words. They sang it to the people in the church.

"Why this is our own music!" cried the listeners delightedly. "This music speaks to our hearts!" And almost at once they could sing the new words.

Then they began to remember other old songs. They began to fit Christian words to the old tunes.

But most of all they still love the new-old song that the children in Abraham's village sang.

"I have heard good news today!"

"Oh! Who told you?"

"God's Word!"

"Christian, oh, who told you?"

"God's Word!"

And they still love to go on with verse after verse, singing the Bible stories and teachings, telling what God's Word has taught them.

2: The Bible a Gateway

China

Honorable Artist sat under the flowering plum tree on a mountainside of China. He was deep in thought. He was planning a picture.

The picture-planning needed deep thought. It was not an ordinary picture that he was going to paint, with delicate strokes of his brush. It was not going to be a picture of the plum blossoms framing the pagoda on the distant hill. Nor was it to be of the frog sitting on the lily pad among the rushes in the pool at the side of the garden. The picture would not show some kindly white-beard of Chinese history, engaged in playing chess with his friends. Nor was it to be a dragon, sporting in the cloud-filled valley of a thousand smokes.

No, it was to be quite different. It was to be a picture of the Bible itself.

"Now how am I to make a picture of the Bible that anyone will want to gaze upon?" mused Honorable Artist. "A picture of the Bible should say something to the people, not merely show what a Bible looks like."

So he sat and thought, and thought, and thought. And the plum blossom petals drifted down and lodged on his shoulders and on his hair till he looked as though spring snow had descended upon him.

At last he had an idea. "The Bible," he said, "is just like a doorway. It is a gate. When I go through the gateway to my father's house, I act in that house as he would like to have me act. I talk about matters in which he is interested. I do things in his way and not in mine. And because my father is rich in wisdom and his ways are right ways, there is peace and joy and harmony within the walls of my father's court-yard."

Honorable Artist tapped his fingers restlessly against the stone bench on which he was sitting. They began to long for the brush to put into color and line and form the idea that was being born in his mind.

"The Bible is like that gateway. It is the entrance to God's city, the city where men try to do what is pleasing to God." Honorable Artist began to feel excited as his idea grew.

"What if I pictured the Bible itself as a gate?" he asked himself, "and people walking through it to the city of God? I could show the streets of the city with people happy and content and useful and kind. I can show people—oh, all sorts of people—hurrying to the gateway."

Then he paused. "Of course, not all people use the Bible. Some do not want to walk and live in the city of God. They prefer to go in ways that are not God's ways. They do not want to find in the Bible the way to God's city of living."

His fingers had hold of a brush now. Honorable Artist did not wait longer to begin his painting.

After a while it was finished. Honorable Artist was content.

When people saw the picture they said at first, "Ah! How interesting! What a quaint idea!" But when they had looked at it longer they became quiet. They began to study it. It began to give them the thoughts the artist had had.

"Honorable Artist has given us a beautiful and true idea," they would say. They would go home then and take each one his Bible from the place where it was kept. Each would begin to read it, and some of them found for the first time in their lives that the Bible was truly the gateway to the beautiful city—the city of God.

3: Seven Pieces of Silk

India

JOHN BOX walked slowly through the crowds in the bazaar of a town of India. The people were gathering for a big *mela*, a religious fair, and everyone was happy.

John wandered along the lines of booths. He stopped to buy some of the flat wheat bread that he liked so much. He tossed a copper coin to a man who was cooking *sev*, the hot, spicy, little crunchy bits of goodness that he ate as if they were peanuts. For a few minutes he watched a dancing bear solemnly performing to the great delight of the children and the grownups gathered around. People were shouting and calling to their friends. They were teasing and laughing at the little mishaps that happened to those who were setting up their camps and stalls.

Now and again a fakir, a religious wanderer, came by. With downcast eyes he would walk along, holding out his bowl for the devout to place within it whatever food they cared to spare for him. Other fakirs sat in quiet thought about the gods, underneath a tree or beside the roadway. They took no part in the fair, but every morning and every evening they made some offering to the gods of the place.

John Box was a religious wanderer, too, but of a different sort. He, too, went from fair to fair. He took with him, wherever he went, a big package of books. He had Bibles and New Testaments. He had copies of *Matthew* and *Mark* and *Luke* and *John* and the *Acts* and the *Epistles* printed in the language of the people of that part of India. They were gay little booklets in pink and green and blue and yellow and red and purple covers. Each little booklet had a different color.

"You are drawing water to quench your thirst," John would call out as he came to the big well where people were busy drawing water in their big earthenware jars. "Here is something to satisfy the thirst of your souls! Buy these little books. They will tell you of Jesus, who is like water to those who are thirsty."

Often someone would bring out a little copper coin and buy a booklet and go away reading it. Sometimes someone would be curious about what John had said and ask him to explain more about it. Then John would stand at the well-curb and preach of Jesus and of God's love.

As he saw offerings of water being poured over the stone images of the gods, John would say softly, "You have traveled many miles, good pilgrims, to make offerings and to seek forgiveness of the gods for your sins. Here is a book that will tell you of the great and only God, who so loved sinful mankind that he sent his own Son to save them from their sins. Buy and read, and find forgiveness and peace."

Then perhaps one of the pilgrims, whose search for God had been long and fruitless as he wandered from holy place to holy place, would lift weary eyes to John. And John would squat down beside him on the dusty grass and talk to him of God. He would tell him of the Bible that brings God's message of love and forgiveness.

It was on the second day of the *mela* that a smiling fakir came up to John.

"Greetings! A thousand greetings!" he said, joining his hands to *salaam* to John, as if he were an old and well loved friend, "I have been looking for you, O Seller-of-Books, for almost a year."

John returned the greeting and wracked his brain to try to remember who the man might be. No memory came to enlighten him.

"You do not remember me? Why should you? One among

thousands. But I will remind you and you will remember," said the fakir.

"Wait!" said John. "It was at a *mela*—"

"At Jalpech!" prompted the fakir.

"And I sold you a Gospel." John was beginning to recall the time and the man.

"The Gospel of *Luke*," supplied the fakir. "And ever since then I have been traveling from one *mela* to another, trying to find you. I want another booklet of the same nature, if there is one." He looked earnestly at John. "This Gospel of *Luke*—it is a book very, very good for the soul."

"So I, too, have found it," agreed John. "And there are three others much like it, by Matthew and Mark and John."

"Then I will buy. But first come with me to my little hut," said the fakir, "and I shall show you something."

They walked through the gay, clamoring, chattering crowds of people, hearing none of their noise. They talked instead of the story that Luke had written down.

"Never, never have I heard such an account," said the fakir. "And you said that it is true, not just written down for the amazement of people?"

"It is a true account," John assured him.

"Wonderful! Wonderful!" murmured the fakir. "See you, O Seller-of-Books. For many years I have wandered. From the shrines of south India, to the holy places in the high mountains where snow lies, have I gone. From the steamy delta of the Ganges, to the place where the sun sets like a ball of fire in the great salt water, have I traveled, seeking peace and understanding—ever seeking peace and the knowledge of God. And all in vain! Then, on a day, your voice came to my ears, offering a little booklet for sale. Because it was small and cheap, and the color of the cover pleased my eyes, I bought the little Gospel of *Luke*. I found in its pages what I had searched for through long years of my life."

They had come to the tiny leaf-and-branch shelter that the fakir had made for himself. In it were a couple of blankets, some foodstuff, and a small wooden box, hidden in a hole dug in the earth of the floor.

"Sit," invited the fakir.

The two men squatted down facing each other on the smooth earth.

The fakir put the box between them. With reverent hands he opened it. Inside was something wrapped in a brilliant piece of green silk.

The fakir slipped the silk wrapping from the package. A red silk wrapping lay beneath.

"Wonder what he has, all wrapped up in silk," said John to himself. "Must be some jewel, or some relic from a shrine. I've never seen anything done up like this. Reminds me of the blue and red covering they sometimes put on the sacred Hindu books in the temples."

Off came the red silk wrapping. Below was another, shimmering with soft color.

Then came a fourth and a fifth and a sixth and, at last, a seventh!

The package was tiny now, and John's curiosity was high. Seven pieces of silk! What could it be that had to have such honor in its wrappings! It must be something of extreme value!

Now the fakir was removing the last piece of silk. John could see what lay in the man's hands, with the silk flowing away from under it. It was the little Gospel of *Luke,* worn with much reading but clean as the day on which it was bought.

"Every day," said the fakir, "I open this holy book. I read a few sentences in it. Then I preach to my followers about its teachings. Seller-of-Books, my heart turns with love and longing to Jesus. You are a follower of his. I, too, would follow him, for he is the only true way to God. And through him I find God and forgiveness and peace."

John's heart sang, for there is no happiness greater than the happiness of having helped someone to know of God and to become a follower of Jesus. Forgotten were all the weary hours when no one seemed interested in his message. Forgotten were the days when no one would buy the books.

Far into the night they talked, the Seller-of-Books and the new disciple of Jesus.

When the *mela* ended and John went on to the next place, he left behind in the hands of the new Christian more copies of the Gospel of *Luke*. "Give them to your followers," he said, "that those who can do so may read for themselves." And to the fakir he gave a Gospel of *Matthew*. "Read it," he told him, "and think about its message until such time as we two can meet once more."

4: The Prize Bible

India

TEACHER Miss Sahiba stood up in front of the school. "A great honor has come to our school," she said, smiling. "Let me tell you about it."

All the little girls, sitting cross-legged on the mission school floor looked up to listen. They were proud of their school and they thought it the very finest in all the country of India.

"You know," said the Miss Sahiba, "that a new translation of the Bible has been made into Urdu." Urdu was the language that all the little girls spoke, so of course they had heard about it. "The translation is finished," went on the Miss Sahiba. "It has been printed on pages. The pages have been bound into books."

Everyone smiled. What a happy thing that was! Murriam asked a question. "Could we see a copy?"

"Many copies!" said the Miss Sahiba. "But this is the wonderful piece of news. Listen well! The very first, yes, the very first Bible to be finished was set to one side. It was taken to His Excellency the Viceroy. His Excellency the Viceroy has written his name in it, and another name as well. What name do you think he has written?"

No one could guess.

"Because our school is one of the best in India, this first Bible is to be given to one of the girls of our school—the one who was at the top of the class. Her name was sent to the Viceroy and he has written her name in the new Bible. That name is Yasmeen!"

Yasmeen's black eyes opened wide with surprise. She could hardly believe it. She had won first place! And her name had been written into the first Bible of the new Urdu translation. What an honor!

Everyone began to talk at once. Everyone was delighted. Everyone loved Yasmeen and was glad of the honor that had come to her.

"That is not all," said the Miss Sahiba.

Everyone stopped talking. No one moved a finger, or shook a tinkling bracelet, or rustled a garment.

"The Bible is to come here to the school. It is to be given as a gift to Yasmeen."

"Oh! Oh! Oh!" whispered Yasmeen. "To be my very own!"

"It has in it Yasmeen's name and the name of His Excellency the Viceroy," said Teacher Miss Sahiba. "It is precious also because it is the very first of the new Bibles."

The girls could hardly wait for the Bible to come to the school. Each one wanted to see it. Each one wanted to read in it. Even the little ones worked hard to learn to read some of the Bible verses from the lesson books so that when the Bible came they would be able to read them. They knew that Yasmeen would let them look at her prize before she took it home.

At last the postman, when he came striding up the long tree-lined walk to the school, carried the long-awaited parcel. "This must be something of importance," said he. "Some one has to sign for it."

All the girls, talking at once, told him what it was. They knew the postman well. Was he not the father of Murriam, and did he not greet each one by name on Sunday mornings when they came to church school?

"I should like to see it some day," he said. "But today I cannot wait. There are many letters in my bag yet to be delivered." He hurried down the road.

The girls all crowded round Teacher Miss Sahiba as she

opened the package. They all danced with excitement as the seals were broken and the string cut and the package opened. And then they saw it! There it lay on the lap of the Miss Sahiba—the new Urdu Bible!

She lifted it up. "Look!" she said. And then, "I think that we shall let Yasmeen open it first," she added.

Yasmeen ran quickly to wash her hands, and the Miss Sahiba smiled with approval. "That is good. We honor our Bibles when we do not touch them with soiled hands," she said. Yasmeen was soon back and standing before her.

Yasmeen took the Bible. She held it in her own hands. Slowly she opened it to the front, and there where all could see, was her name, and the name of His Excellency, the Viceroy of all India. Yasmeen drew in a long breath.

Then she looked troubled.

"Teacher Miss Sahiba, it is a most beautiful book. And in my home there is no place to keep such a treasure. The roof sometimes leaks when the rain comes. Only in the chest is anything safe. If it is put in the chest, it will be hard to get when we want it."

Now that very thing had been bothering Teacher Miss Sahiba. She knew just what kind of home Yasmeen lived in. The new Bible would not last very long there. Of that she was sure.

"Would you like the Bible to be kept here at the school?" she asked softly. "Is that what you would like, Yasmeen?"

"Oh, yes!" Yasmeen looked up happily. "It would be quite safe here. We could all read from it."

Then Yasmeen had another idea. "I shall take some beautiful blue cloth my mother has given me," she said. "I shall make a cover for the Bible."

"That will be exactly right," agreed the Miss Sahiba.

So Yasmeen sewed busily in the days that followed. Her mother helped her to cut the blue linen cloth to the right size. And with tiny, tiny stitches, so small that you could hardly see them, Yasmeen made the cover.

When it was done, her mother helped her to slip the corners of the Bible into the right places and the blue cover fitted as smoothly as the brown skin lay on Yasmeen's own soft, pretty hand. "Ah, how handsome!" admired her mother.

"A beautiful cover for a most precious book," agreed her father.

Yasmeen's family were at school the next day. They had come to be present when the Bible was dedicated and put in its place of honor.

There was a little service of worship. The girls sang praise to God. One of the older ones read from the new Bible, opening it on the stand where it had been placed. Then Yasmeen, dressed in her best clothing, all green with golden threads woven into the borders, stood up beside the Bible. She laid her slender little hand on the open Book.

"Dear Lord," she prayed, "it is wonderful to have this new Bible in our own dear Urdu language. We are proud to have the very first copy that was finished and ready for people to use. We are going to keep the Bible here. We are going to read it every day. Bless us and help us to understand the teaching that is in our Bible. We ask for Jesus' sake, Amen."

After the service everyone went to have a look at the beautiful Bible. Each girl read a verse from it. Even the littlest ones read the verses they had been practising.

Then the Bible was closed. It lay quiet on the stand. Its blue cover shone in the fingers of sunlight that touched it.

Yasmeen sighed with happiness because of the honor that had come to the school and to her, and mostly because she had thought of a way for all the girls to be able to use the precious gift that had been given her.

5: The Bible Bought by Music

United States

THE office door opened part way. There in the opening stood an old, old Negro. He was so old that he was bent almost double. But his eyes were bright and shining.

"You want something?" the young Negro man at the desk asked courteously. "Something we can do for you? Come on in."

The Old One shuffled in. His clothing was plainly what others had thrown away. His shoes were barely holding together.

"You-all sell Bibles here?"

"Yes, indeed."

"You-all want I should tell you about me?"

"I'd like to hear." The young man was curious about this old, old grandfather who wanted to tell something about himself.

"Seems like it's too long ago for me to remember. Back in the days of slavery. Born a slave, I was." He looked up sharply to see whether he was believed.

The young man nodded. Old One seemed to him to be old enough to be Methuselah.

"Born a slave! And my master he said no child on his plantation should learn to read or write. But me, I had a hankering for learning. And learn I did. And got whipped often enough for being catched with a book, I did." The Old One chuckled. "Didn't stop me none!"

He went on presently. "Then old master gave my daddy to be a slave to his daughter, and me with him. And she was different. She 'lowed me to learn to read and write. Said couldn't no harm come from learning to read the

Bible. No more it did." He smiled at the recollection. "Learned to read it. Learned to love it."

The old man looked up. "Ain't got no Bible now. And I want one powerful bad. Seems like now's I'm too old to work, I yet could read, did I but have me a Bible."

The young man was interested. Was the Old One going to beg for a Bible as a gift? If so, he had a few Bibles he could give away, provided he thought it wise.

"Ain't got no money, young man. But I sure do want a Bible. If it's any way possible, I can earn one. See, I got here my flute to play some tunes to earn it. Used to be people paid me to have me play tunes on my flute for their dancing feet."

At that his look became anxious. He had come, so sure that his flute-playing would earn what he wanted so badly. But now he was not sure. Would it? Probably no one wanted music for dancing feet, here in this Bible Society office. People were working, not dancing.

"What can you play, Uncle?" asked the young man softly.

"Dance tunes and church tunes," answered the Old One hopefully.

"Play the church tunes, then."

The old, old man lifted the flute to his lips. He drew in a long breath, and the quavering notes floated out. His tones were true, and as he played the hymn tunes, the young man seemed to see the little slave boy, poring over the Bible, in danger of a whipping and often getting one.

He went quickly to the case where the gift Bibles were. He brought one of them and laid it in the old man's hands. "Here, Uncle. Will this one do?"

The old man's flute was forgotten now. It lay silent on the table while his eager hands reached out for the Bible.

"You could? You could let me have it? 'Thout any price?"

"I reckon you've earned it, Uncle," smiled the young man. "Even without the hymn tunes, you earned it way back when you took whippings to learn to read it."

The young man stood at the office door. He watched the Old One go down the street. He wasn't shuffling now. He was walking so slowly he hardly moved. But the Book was open in his hands and he was slowly reading out loud as he went.

The young man turned back to his desk. "I wish they all wanted Bibles as badly as that Old One," he said to himself.

6: The Dusted Bible

United States

Yes," said the woman at the door, "I can let you rent a room here while you go to school. But I can't undertake to keep it cleaned. You'll have to do that yourself. The rent will be less that way." Her calm brown eyes looked at John as if they liked him.

John took the room. He was a country boy and he had to live in town if he wanted to go to high school. He didn't care much about the idea of keeping his room clean, but if he had to, he guessed he could do it. Anyway, he wouldn't have to clean it often.

Several days after he had moved in he came home from school and went to his room. There on the table was a Bible. It wasn't his. Someone must have laid it there.

He went to look at it. On top of the Bible there was a note. "Here is the best book in the world. I hope you will read in it every day."

John smiled a sour smile. Not likely! He had not used a Bible since he was in the junior class in the little country Sunday school where he sometimes went with his grandmother.

"Much use the Bible is," he muttered, and threw himself down on the unmade bed to read a story.

Two weeks went by. John didn't do a thing about keeping his room clean. The bed went unmade; the floor was unswept; dust was thick over everything.

But as the days went by John noticed an odd thing. No matter how thick the dust lay on dresser and table and floor, the Bible was always dusted and clean. His hostess was patiently waiting for him to keep his part of the bargain about caring for his own room. But she was going in every day and dusting off the copy of the Bible that she still hoped he would some day read.

John began to be bothered by the looks of his room. He wished it were clean. But he did nothing about it. He wasn't doing well in school, either. There was no one to make him work and he was spending more time playing games and reading storybooks than studying. Somehow he just wasn't managing very well.

One day John came home and stood in the doorway of his room and looked at it. In the midst of all the untidyness lay the dusted Bible. For a minute he stood staring at it. Then he flung himself into a chair and took the Bible in his hands. He knew where some of the verses and stories were that he had learned when he was in church school. He turned to one or two of them.

All at once things began to clear up in his mind. He knew that he'd been loafing. He'd been cheating on the agreement that he had made about keeping his room clean. He'd been lazy about it and about his school work, too.

There was a verse somewhere in the Bible, he knew, that went something like, "Whatsoever thy hand findeth to do, do it with thy might." Perhaps it would be a good idea to read the Bible and to think about God and about the way that Jesus lived and worked. Perhaps that would help him to straighten out his own way of doing things.

John got up. He walked over to the closet. His hostess had hung a duster there for him to use. It was as fresh as the day he had moved into the room. John reached for it and dusted off the table. He put the Bible back in its place. Then he went downstairs for a broom and mop. He worked until the room was clean.

School went better after that. John learned to rule himself. His room was untidy sometimes, but mostly it was clean and in good order. The Bible still lay on the table, but there weren't many days when he didn't dip into it.

Years went by. One day John stood up in the pulpit of a little church. He opened the pulpit Bible to the lesson of the day. In a clear, strong voice he read the message to the congregation.

While the choir sang, his thoughts went back to that day when he picked up the dusted Bible in his untidy room.

"Blessings on my good hostess," he thought to himself. "I wonder what she would think if she saw me today, preaching my first sermon and reading the wonderful words of the Bible to the congregation of my first church?"

7: The Blind Leper

Latin America

Aɴᴛᴏɴɪᴏ lived in a leper colony. He had been there for years and years. Antonio was a leper. Nothing had been able to stop the disease.

Yet Antonio was a happy leper. For one thing he was a Christian. For a second reason he could read, and none of the other lepers could do that. For a third thing he had a Bible. Antonio's greatest joy was to read the Bible to the other lepers.

One day he noticed that he was having trouble reading. His eyes bothered him. It was not long before he became very anxious about it. The doctor looked at his eyes. He spoke very slowly, as though he hated to let the words come from his lips. "You are going blind, Antonio. There's nothing we can do about it."

Antonio sat still, as if he were frozen. Blind! He would be a blind leper! No longer would he be able to find his way from hut to hut carrying his Bible. No longer would he be able to read to the other lepers from its precious pages.

For days Antonio sat in miserable silence. How could he bear it? But one day a thought came to him. His eyes were getting dim, but he was not yet blind. His mind was as clear as ever. "I can learn some of the Bible," thought Antonio. "Then, when I am blind, I can still find my way from house to house and I can recite the words of the Bible to my friends who love to hear them."

He took his Bible in his hands. What part should he choose to learn first? Antonio turned page after page. How he loved this psalm! How majestic were these words from *Isaiah!* What wonderful teaching Jesus gave in this chapter! The story of

Paul was so loved by his comrades! Which should he learn first?

Antonio murmured, "Which has a place in my heart? Which verses are worth putting there forever?" He chose first one passage, then another, and a third. He began to learn the first passage. He worked hard. Soon—because it does not take long to learn what you really want to—he could say it without a mistake. He began on the second. Not long after he was working on the third.

When his friends heard what he was doing, they began to hobble to his hut.

"Antonio," an old man said, "are you learning the Eighth Psalm? Because I must have that one."

"Not yet," said Antonio, "but I will learn it next."

The old man went away satisfied, and a group of children came running up.

"Learn about Jesus and the children," they begged. "Learn about the shepherds and the wise men."

"I will learn, and you must learn with me," said Antonio.

"Are you planning to learn the Ten Commandments?" asked a father.

"It is on my list," answered Antonio.

"We must have the Shepherd Psalm," said one of the mothers.

"I have already learned it," smiled Antonio.

"Do you know the words of Jesus about the heavenly home?" asked an old woman. She was suffering a great deal, and how she loved Jesus' words about God's house in which there would be room for all!

"I will learn it," promised Antonio.

So, day after day, he put into his heart and into his mind Bible passages that those leper Christians loved.

As his eyes became dimmer, he read less and he spent more time learning. Then at last came the day to which he had looked forward with such sorrow. When he opened his Bible, not one word could he make out.

But somehow he was not so sad as he had thought he would be. "The days of learning are over," he said to himself. "Now I can give the messages to others."

Antonio could still see to find his way to the huts of his friends. With the clear sunlight falling on his smiling face, he went forth. As he came to the hut of his nearest friend, the same old greeting rang out that he had heard so often.

"Antonio is come! Antonio is here! He will speak to us from God's Word! Welcome! Welcome!"

Antonio sat down. His useless eyes could not see to read. But his voice was firm as he began to repeat verse after beloved verse from the book he loved best.

"When God's Word is in our hearts it is good," he said.

And those gathered around to hear agreed with him. "God's Word in our hearts. That is good," they said.

8: Headaches of a Translator

How can we say *camel* in the language the Eskimos use?" wondered the translators of the Bible in the far north. "There is no such word in this language and nobody in this part of the world has ever seen such an animal." That was before the days of moving pictures. The translators rubbed their puzzled heads.

The same thing happens all over the world today—on the shores of the highest lake in the world, far back in the jungles of steamy tropics, on faraway islands, or in the desolate, frozen desert plateaus of inland China. Every time a translator sits down to put the Bible into some other language, he works until his head fairly aches, trying to find the right words. "How shall I say this? What is the word for that? How shall I express this idea so that it means anything at all to a people that have never had it?"

Here are a few of the words that translators have found it hard to translate, and here are some of the ways in which words and ideas have finally been translated:

"By the *grace* of God," a translator in the South Sea Islands read in his English Bible. And in another place, "the Lord be *gracious* unto thee."

"Is there any way of saying that in the language of the people of these islands? Is there any way of saying it and expressing the real meaning of it?"

Finally a word was found. It meant a *gift*. But not just any gift. Oh, no! It meant more than that.

It meant a free gift—one that the person receiving it had not earned in any way at all. Nor did he have to pay for it. But it meant even more than that.

It meant a gift of kindness displayed to someone who deserved exactly the opposite.

Now, however in the world did the translator find that word?

He first heard the expression one day when he gave something to a man. His South Seas friends objected.

"Why," they protested, "did you give that man that object? He is your enemy!"

And then they used the long-sought-after word. "You have displayed kindness to someone who deserved the exact opposite—*Nau ku efea goo!*"

Here are some questions that translators in different parts of the world have had to ask themselves, and here also are the answers they found:

What word shall we use for *gate?*
   The *mouth-of-the-road.*
And what for *east?*
   Where-morning-is-born.
How shall we say *our conscience?*
   Heart-knowing-evil.
What about *clouds?*
   Darkness-of-rain.
What shall we do about *kiss?* The people here do not kiss one another.
   They *blow-in-the-ear.*
As *white as snow* just doesn't mean a thing.
   But *white-as-egrets* does.

"Have they no word for *saved?*" the translator worried. "Jesus *saves* us from our sins. It is one of the most important truths in the Bible. We must have the right word for *save.*"

For months he questioned one person after another. But it was in vain.

Then one day a hunter came home, badly wounded but able to recover. "I was attacked by a lion," he told them excitedly. "But some other hunters came along and I was *saved*."

"Ah!" said the translator. "He was attacked but he was *saved*! There is my word!"

"Master," said his helpers, "now we understand what you mean by the teaching about Jesus saving people. All these months you have been trying to teach it to us, but the words meant nothing. Surely this is the word that we must put down in the writing of the Bible into our language. This is the word that will speak to the hearts of our people."

9: Translation on Top of a Ladder

Northern Rhodesia

Words! Words! Words!" groaned Dr. Edwin Smith. "If I only had the words, I could get this translation done in a hurry."

Dr. Smith and his African helpers were busy putting the Bible into the Ila language, so that the people who spoke that tongue could read and understand it.

One of the African helpers looked at Dr. Smith with sympathy. "Too many words needed for our Ila language," he suggested. "Not have words in Ila for some thoughts. Not understand what words in your language mean."

"I know"—Dr. Smith tapped the table with his pencil— "but there are words for some of the ideas if we could just find them."

"This English word *trust*." The African returned to their problem. " 'What time I am afraid, I will put my trust in thee.' *Trust!* No word for that in my language."

Again and again Dr. Smith tried to explain the meaning of *trust*. He put it one way; he put it another way. But not with all his explanations could he make the idea clear enough to get a word for *trust* from his companions.

Dr. Smith stretched his arms above his head. "Enough for one day," he said. "Let's get to work and paper that room."

Missionaries have to be jacks-of-all-trades. They have to know how to do everything, from treating snakebite to translating the Bible.

The African men and boys looked doubtfully at the wall-paper. They had no idea how to get it onto the wall. So presently Dr. Smith was perched on top of a very rickety ladder, pasting wallpaper onto the wall.

The workmen looked at him with admiration. They stood around to watch the missionary work at something they themselves could not do at all.

Dr. Smith listened to their softly spoken remarks, amused by what they were saying while they thought him too busy working to hear them.

Then suddenly he stiffened to attention. What was that he had just heard?

He repeated the words of one of the workmen in his own mind.

" 'If I were the missionary, I wouldn't trust my life to that old ladder. He'll break his neck.' "

Trust! The word he'd been asking and asking and asking for! There it was!

He turned around on the ladder. " 'What time I am afraid, I will put my trust in thee,' " he said, using the Ila word that the workman had just used.

The men stared at him. Then one of the African helpers gave a shout.

"*Trust!* Is that what your English word means, Bwana?" He said the Bible verse over and over, putting in the Ila word. " 'What time I am afraid, I will put my trust in thee.' " Again and again he said it, thinking hard. "Now I know what you are talking about, Bwana. Now we know what you mean when you say '*trust* God.' "

Dr. Smith went on with his paper hanging. The paste was wet and the paper would be ruined if he stopped. But he could hardly wait to get down off that ladder to which he was trusting his life and write down his new-found word in its place in the Bible translation he was making in the Ila language.

PART IV: BIBLE WORDS IN MANY TONGUES

I: The Lord's Prayer

In the England of a Thousand Years Ago

ALFRED the Great was king of England. That was before the year A.D. 1000. In fact, it was a little more than a thousand years ago.

King Alfred was a valiant soldier. He threw back the Danish raiders and brought peace to England.

He was a good man and a good king. In addition to being good, he was wise. Valiant, good, and wise!

Alfred was a Christian. He wanted his people to be Christian. He spent much time translating parts of the Bible into Anglo-Saxon, which was the language used in those days in that part of the world.

You all know the Lord's Prayer. Would you like to see how it looked in the Anglo-Saxon of King Alfred's day? On the next page you will find this Anglo-Saxon version. Beside it we are printing the same Lord's Prayer in what is called Early English. That was the language used in England years later. You will find some words that you can make out in each of the translations. Try pronouncing the sounds. When *our iche-days-bred* is put into today's English, it is spelled *our each day's bread*. As we repeat the Lord's Prayer today we say *our daily bread*.

Try to make out some of the other words and phrases.

Following these two versions, you will find the Lord's Prayer as Tyndale wrote it, a modern translation by Goodspeed, and the way in which it appears in French and Spanish.

Anglo-Saxon Version

Uren Fader dhis art in heof-
nas,
Sic gehalged dhin noma,
To oymedh dhin ric,
Sic dhin uuilla sue is in heof-
nas and in eardho.
Vren hlaf ofer uuirthe sel vs
to daeg,
And forgef us scylda urna,
Sue uue forgefan sculdgun
vrum,
And no inleadh vridk in cost-
nung al gefrig vrich from
ifle.

Early English Version

Fader oure that art in heve,

I-halgeed be thi nome,
I-cume thi kinereiche
Y-worthe thi wylle also is in
hevene so be on erthe,
Our iche-days-bred gif us
today,
And forgif us oure gultes,
Also we forgifet oure gultare,

And ne led ows nowth into
fondyngge, Auth ales ows
of harme,
So be hit.

From Tyndale's Version

O oure father which arte in heven,
Halowed be thy name.
Let thy kyngdō come.
Thy wyll be fulfilled, as well in erth, as hit ys in heven.
Geve vs this daye oure dayly breade.
And forgeve vs oure treaspases, evē as we forgeve thē which treas-
pas vs.
Leede vs not into temptacion.
But delyvre vs ffrom yvell, Amen.

A Modern Translation

Our Father in heaven,
Your name be revered!
Your kingdom come!
Your will be done on earth as it is done in heaven!
Give us today bread for the day,

And forgive us our debts, as we have forgiven our debtors.
And do not subject us to temptation,
But save us from the evil one.

The Lord's Prayer
With Response

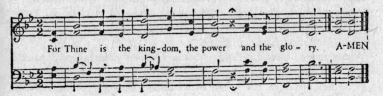

For Thine is the king-dom, the power and the glo-ry. A-MEN

Our Father who art in heaven, hallowed be thy name,
   For thine is the kingdom, the power and the glory.
Thy kingdom come on earth as it is in heaven,
   For thine is the kingdom, the power and the glory.
Thy will be done on earth as it is in heaven.
   For thine is the kingdom, the power and the glory.

Give us this day our daily bread,
   For thine is the kingdom, the power and the glory.
And forgive us our debts as we forgive our debtors,
   For thine is the kingdom, the power and the glory.
Lead us not into temptation, but deliver us from evil,
   For thine is the kingdom, the power and glory. Amen.

In French

Notre Père qui es aux cieux; que ton nom soit sanctifié;

Que ton règne vienne; que ta volonté soit faite sur la terre comme
au ciel;

Donne-nous aujourd'hui notre pain quotidien,

Et pardonne-nous nos offenses, comme aussi nous pardonnons à ceux
qui nous ont offensés;

Et ne nous induis pas en tentation; mais délivre-nous du mal; car
c'est à toi qu'appartiennent dans tous les siècles le règne, la puis-
sance et la gloire. Amen.

In Spanish

Padre nuestro, que estás en los cielos: sea santificado tu nombre.

Venga tu reino: sea hecha tu voluntad, como en el cielo, así tambien en la tierra.

Dános hoy nuestro pan cotidiano.

Y perdónanos nuestras deudas, como tambien nosotros perdonamos
á nuestros deudores.

Y no nos metas en tentacion, mas líbranos de mal; porque tuyo es
el reino, y el poder, y la gloria, por todos los siglos. Amen.

2: The Twenty-third Psalm

Paraphrase for Navajo Indians

The great Father above a Shepherd Chief is, the same as I am he
is, and with him I want not.

He throws out to me a rope, and the name of the rope is love,
and he draws me, and he draws me, and he draws me to where the
grass is green and the water not dangerous; and I eat and lie down
satisfied.

Sometimes my heart is very weak and falls down, but he lifts
it up again and draws me into a good road. His Name is Wonderful.

Sometime, it may be very soon, it may be longer, it may be a
long, long time, he will draw me into a place between the mountains. It is dark there, but I'll not draw back. I'll be afraid not, for
it is in there between those mountains that the Shepherd Chief will

meet me, and the hunger I have felt in my heart all through this life will be satisfied. Sometimes he makes the love rope into a whip, but afterwards he gives me a staff to lean on.

He spreads a table before me with all kinds of food. He puts his hands upon my head and all the "tired" is gone. My cup he fills till it runs over.

What I tell you is true; I lie not. These roads that are "away ahead" will stay with me through this life, and afterwards I will go to live in the "Big Tepee" and sit down with the Shepherd Chief forever.

— *Translation by Isabel Crawford. Reprinted from* Ganado News Bulletin

Paraphrase by a Junior High Group

The Lord is my guide;
He supplies my needs.
He carefully cares for me
Trying to find the best for me.
He keeps me on the right path;
The path of righteousness.
Even though I am dying, I shall not fear death
Because God is with me always.
I shall consider my enemies
Because God is good to me.
God's goodness and mercy will follow me
Wherever I go,
And I shall worship him forever.

—*Utica Presbytery Junior High Camp,* 1944

3: James 1:22 in Nine Languages

ENGLISH
    Be ye doers of the word, and not hearers only.

DANISH
    Men vorder Ordets Gørere og ikke alene dets Hørere.

DUTCH
    En weest daders des woords en niet alleen hoorders.

FRENCH

Mettez en pratique la parole, et ne vous contentez pas de l'écouter.

GERMAN

Seid aber Thäter des Worts, und nicht Hörer allein.

ITALIAN

E siate facitori della parola, e non solo uditori.

POLISH

A bądzcie czynicielmi słowa, a nie słuchaczami tylko.

SPANISH

Mas sed hacedores de la palabra, y no tan solamente oidores.

SWEDISH

Men varen ordets görare, och icke allenast dess hörare.

4: Some Verses to Read

BIBLE VERSES ABOUT THE BIBLE

    Deuteronomy 6: 6, 7
    Psalms 119: 11, 105, 169
    Psalms 68: 11
    Hebrews 4: 12

STORIES ABOUT THE USE OF THE BIBLE

The book of the law found in Josiah's reign: *II Kings* 22: 1-13; 23: 1-3.

Ezra reads to his people from the book of the law: *Nehemiah* 8.

The king destroys the book that Jeremiah wrote: *Jeremiah* 36: 11-16, 23-24.

Jesus reads aloud from the Scriptures in the synagogue: *Luke* 4: 16-21.

How the boy Timothy was taught the Scriptures: *II Timothy* 1: 1; 3: 14-16.

A foreigner reads some verses from the Scriptures: *Acts* 8: 26-38.

STORIES ABOUT THE WRITING OF THE BIBLE

A prophet writes a book: *Jeremiah* 36: 1-4, 17-18.

Luke writes a Gospel: *Luke* 1: 1-3.

Luke writes another book: *Acts* 1: 1, 2.

Tertius writes a letter at Paul's dictation: *Romans* 16: 22.

Paul writes a letter himself: *Philemon* 1.

5: Talking Birch Bark

Over a hundred years ago, James Evans went as a missionary to the Cree Indians who lived around Lake Winnipeg in Canada. The first thing he had to do was to learn their language. Then he invented an alphabet for them, with a system of signs for the sounds of their language. He whittled the signs out of wood and made little clay moulds of each. Into the moulds he poured melted lead from the lining of tea chests. So he got his type. He used birch bark for paper, and ink he made from soot and fish oil. His printing press was the press for storing furs, in the store of the Hudson's Bay Company post. The Indian women sewed the birch-bark leaves together to make the first books in Cree.

The Indians learned to read the printed signs easily. How surprised they were when they understood the meaning of the words they read! "The birch bark talks," they said.

The Cree alphabet is still in use. You will find a story about it on page 34 of this book.

Cree Alphabet and a Verse in Cree

On the following two pages you will find the Cree alphabet as it was worked out by James Evans and a Bible sentence in the Cree language. See if you can read the verse, with the help of the vocabulary that follows.

CREE SYLLABIC ALPHABET

Syllables				Occasional Endings
▽ a	△ e	▷ o	◁ ä	′ - t
▽ pa	∧ pe	> po	< pä	‵ - k
∪ ta	∩ te	⊃ to	⊂ tä	″ - h
９ ka	Ρ ke	d ko	b kä	⊃ - n
⌐ cha	Γ che	∪ cho	∪ chä	∩ - s.
⌐ ma	Γ me	⊥ mo	∟ mä	○ - w.
⊖ na	σ ne	⊃ no	⌒ nä	*Example*
⅃ sa	⌐ se	⌐ so	⅃ sä	∧ - pe
⟨ ya	⌐ ye	⌐ yo	⊐ yä	∧‵ - pek

Note: *ä is pronounced ah.*

BIBLE VERSE IN CREE

ᐁᐢᐱᐦᒋ ᓴᑭᐦᑕᐟ ᑭᓭᒪᓂᑐ ᐊᐢᑭᔨᐤ ᑲ ᑭᐦᐅᐦᒋ ᒣᑭᐟ ᐅᐯᔭᑯᓴᓇ,
ᐊᐃᔭᐠ ᑫᑕᐯᔦᔨᒪᑫ ᐁᑲ ᑭᒋ ᓂᓯᐊᓇᑎᓯᐟ, ᒪᑲ ᑭᒋ ᐊᔭᐟ ᑲᑭᑫ ᐱᒪᑎᓯᐃᐧᐣ.

The first symbol is a triangle and it stands for *a*. The little loop after it means *s*. So the first syllable is *as*.

The upside-down v stands for *pe* and the two little lines after it for *h*. So the second syllable is *peh*.

The third symbol is a little hook that means *che*.

So the whole word is *as-peh-che*. The vocabulary below tells you that this means "So."

See if you can make out the meaning of the rest of the verse.

VOCABULARY

Cree	*English*
a-kä	not
as-peh-che	so
ä-e-yäk	who so ever
äs-ke-yew	the world
ä-yät	he has
ka-tä-pa-ya-ye-mä-ka	believeth on Him
kä	that
kä-ke-ka	everlasting
ke-che	that
keh-oh-che ma-ket	He gave
ke-sa-mä-ne-to	God
mä-kä	but
ne-se-ä-nä-te-set	he shall perish
o-pa-yä-ko-sä-nä	his only begotten son
pe-mä-te-se-en	life
sä-keh-tät	he loved

PART V: WORSHIP MATERIALS

I: Poems and Hymns

The Word of God

The Word of God shall guide my feet,
Wherever I may go;
The Word of God shall teach my heart
The things it ought to know;
The Word of God shall make me strong
And bless me through my whole life long,
And bless me through my whole life long.

The Word of God upon my lips
Helps me to spread the story;
The Word of God before my eyes
Will show me all His glory;
The Word of God within my heart
Will give me strength to do my part,
Will give me strength to do my part.

Our God is with us all the time,
Wherever we may be;
He's helping, guiding, loving
All children, even me.
I'll read His Word and keep His law
And love Him daily more and more,
And love Him daily more and more.

Ships

St. Peter pushed his boat out,
The crowds stood held in thrall,
As Jesus sat in the ship and preached
Good news, good news to them all.

From the little sea
Of Galilee
Over ocean's widest spaces,
East, west, south, north,
Good news sped forth
To the folk of a thousand races.

St. Paul's ship went to the Romans,
Mackey's to Africa's call,
John Williams sailed to the island to take
Good news, good news to them all.

From the little sea
Of Galilee
Over ocean's widest spaces,
East, west, south, north,
Good news sped forth
To the folk of a thousand races.

From a thousand tribes and peoples,
Boys and girls obey the call.
Sent by a fleet of a thousand ships
Good news, good news to them all.

From the little sea
Of Galilee
Over ocean's widest spaces,
Your ships may reach
World's ends to preach
Good news to a thousand races.

Book of Books

Book of books, our people's strength,
Statesman's, teacher's, hero's treasure,
Bringing freedom, speeding truth,
Shedding light that none can measure;
Wisdom comes to those who know thee,
All the best we have we owe thee.

Thank we those who toiled in thought,
Many diverse scrolls completing,
Poets, prophets, scholars, saints,
Each his word from God repeating;
Till they came, who told the story
Of the Word, and showed his glory.

Praise we God, who hath inspired
Those whose wisdom still directs us;
Praise him for the Word made flesh,
For the Spirit who protects us.
Light of knowledge, ever burning,
Shed on us thy deathless learning.

—*Percy Dearmer*

The Bible Helps Me

The Bible helps me know the Friend
Of children everywhere,
Who came to help us understand
Our Father's love and care.

I like the stories that it tells
Of Jesus, doing good;
They help me act in friendly ways
To do the things I should.

Lord, Thy Word Abideth

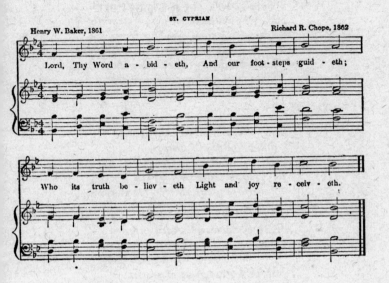

ST. CYPRIAN

Henry W. Baker, 1861   Richard R. Chope, 1862

Lord, Thy Word a - bid - eth, And our foot-steps guid - eth;

Who its truth be - liev - eth Light and joy re - ceiv - eth.

The Bible Is a Treasure Book

The Bible is a treasure book
Of stories that are true:
It tells of people long ago—
Of folks like me and you.

The Bible is a treasure book
Of verses old and new:
Some make us think of lovely things;
Some show us what to do.

The Bible is a treasure book:
It tells how, long ago,
Christ Jesus came to live on earth,
Our Father's love to show.

For Stories Fine and True

We thank thee, O our Father,
For stories fine and true
Of people in the Bible
Who knew and loved thee too.
They learned to serve thee bravely;
To help 'gainst pain and wrong.
They wondered at thy goodness;
They praised in joyous song.

We thank thee, O our Father,
For stories fine and true
Of One who tried so gladly
His Father's work to do.
We like to hear of Jesus,
So brave, so strong in need,
We thank thee for the Bible;
His story there we read.

For Thy Great Book of Stories

For Thy great book of stories
That Thou hast given me
I praise Thee, God our Father,
And thank Thee heartily.

Here I can read of people
Who, marching down the years,
Learned how to pray and trust Thee,
The Friend who always hears.

The people of the Bible
Are glowing lights for me,
To guide my steps and teach me
Thy loving child to be.

The truest book of stories
The world has ever known
Is like a lamp that, lighted,
Through all the world has shone.

2: Prayers

Upon Receiving a Gift of a Bible

Dear God, our loving Father, we hold here in our hands, each one of us, a copy of thy Book. May we each honor his own Bible, and give it a place of honor in his home. May we each come to possess not only the outward form of thy Book but its inward thoughts. May we follow its guidance, as it reveals thy thoughts and thy will for us, thy children. We thank thee that the Bible can be ours, and ask thy blessing on us as we use it. May it lead us ever closer to thee, in whom is light and life and joy everlasting. Amen.

After Examining a Bible in Another Language

Dear God, we cannot read the Bible that we have just seen, but we know that it is read with joy by the people in whose language it is printed. We thank thee for all those who have worked long and hard to put the words of the Bible into the language of many peoples. We thank thee for those who work to take the Bible to others. May the time be not long in coming when every person in the whole wide world may know and treasure thy great Book. May the time come when thy children all over the world read the Bible to find out what is thy will for them, and follow its guidance as best they are able. May we, into whose language the Bible was put so many generations ago, give more and more heed to its teachings and learn to walk in its way, which is thy way. Amen.

After Gathering an Offering to Send Bibles to Others

Dear Lord, we have gathered together some money. It will be used to send Bibles to those who need them. Bless our gift, and may the Bibles that it buys bring a blessing to those to whom they are given. If they have never had Bibles, may they read with joy from thy Word. If they have had too few Bibles, may they be able to study more carefully what is written in thy Book. Bless us and bless them as we study the Bible and learn more about thee and about thy will for us. Amen.

Before Using the Bible in Class

Dear Lord, thou hast given us the Bible to be a lamp unto our feet and a light unto our way. As we study in thy Word today, help us to understand its message. And better than that, guide us to know what it is that we ourselves must do to walk in thy way. May the words of the Bible be to us, this day, a help for our daily living and a guide for our lives.   Amen.

After Reading from the Bible

Dear God, we have just read from thy Word. We thank thee for the Bible. We thank thee that in its pages we find stories of men and women and boys and girls who have loved thee and tried to do what thou wouldst have them do. May we be helped by what we have heard and read to live more nearly as thou wouldst wish. Amen.

Because We Have the Bible

Dear Lord and Father of us all, we thank thee for the Bible. We thank thee for its stories, its songs, and its teachings. May we learn to love it more and more, and find in it help in living as thy children.   Amen.

For Translators

Dear God, we are thinking today of men and women who are working to find the right words in strange languages as they translate the Bible for people who have not had it before in their own tongue. Help the translators to find words that give the right meaning. Give them patience to try and try and try again. Give them great happiness as they work, because it is a joyful thing that they are doing. Bless all those who have a part in the translation, and in the copying, and in the printing, and in the binding, and in the shipping, and in the distributing. And bless those who then read, for the first time in their lives, the stories and teachings of the Bible in their own language.   Amen.

ACKNOWLEDGMENTS

GRATEFUL acknowledgment is made to the following publishers and individuals for permission to quote:

To the American Bible Society for the Anglo-Saxon and Early English versions of the Lord's Prayer, from the *Bible Society Record* for January, 1945;

To the British and Foreign Bible Society for the poem "Ships," from *For Every Land* for March and April, 1944;

To the Oxford University Press for the words of the hymn "Book of Books," by Percy Dearmer, from *Enlarged Songs of Praise;*

To the Presbyterian Board of Christian Education for the words of the hymn "The Word of God," stanza 1 by Nancy Byrd Turner, stanza 2 by Vivien Brown (a junior), stanza 3 by Ruth Manner (a junior), from *Hymns for Junior Worship,* copyright, 1940; for the words of the hymns "The Bible Helps Me," by Mabel Niedermeyer, and "For Thy Great Book of Stories," by Wilhelmina D'A. Stephens, from *Hymns for Primary Worship,* copyright, 1946;

To the University of Chicago Press for the use of the Lord's Prayer as found in *Matthew* 6: 9-13 of *The Bible, An American Translation,* by J. M. Powis Smith and Edgar J. Goodspeed, copyright, 1935;

To Ida Binger Hubbard for the Lord's Prayer with response, from *Junior Quarterly* for April, May, and June, 1945, copyright by the Methodist Publishing House;

To Elizabeth McE. Shields for the words of the hymn "The Bible Is a Treasure Book," from *Hymns for Primary Worship,* copyright, 1944, by Miss Shields;

To Ethel L. Smither for the words of the hymn "For Stories Fine and True."